SOMEBODY ELSE IS ON THE MOON

Somebody Else Is on the Moon

SOMEBODY ELSE IS ON THE MOON

"The Search for Alien Artifacts"

By
George Leonard

A Study in Selenography, whereby an attempt is made to determine whether there is evidence for extraterrestrial activity of space aliens. Illustrated with hundreds of NASA planetary pictures!

ISBN: 978-93-5128-917-3(HB)

First Published in 1976
Indian Reprint in 2017

Published by

Kalpaz Publications
C-30, Satyawati Nagar,
Delhi – 110052
E-mail: kalpaz@hotmail.com
Website: kalpazpublications.com
Ph.: +91-9212142040

Cataloging in Publication Data—DK

Courtesy: D.K. Agencies (P) Ltd. <docinfo@dkagencies.com>

Leonard, George H, author.

Somebody else is on the moon : "the search for alien artifacts" / by George Leonard.

pages cm

Reprint. Originally published: New York : McKay, 1976.

"A study in selenography, whereby an attempt is made to determine whether there is evidence for extraterrestrial activity of space aliens. Illustrated with hundreds of NASA planetary pictures!."

ISBN 9789351289173 (HB)

1. Moon. 2. Life on other planets. I. Title.

QB581.9.L46 2017 DDC 001.94 23

FOREWORD

In 1976 George H Leonard published "Someone Else Is on the Moon" in which he reprinted numerous (blurry) NASA photographs of the lunar surface and suggested that large scale machinery was visible in these pictures. The book was a first in the detailing of so-called alien artifacts thought to be on the Moon and a revelation compared to previous attempts at interpreting lunar oddities as seen by earth based telescopic observers.

Based on NASA photography, George H. Leonard's "SOMEONE ELSE IS ON THE MOON" contains an extraordinary and unbelievable analysis of NASA moon photo's from the early missions.

Mr. Leonard attempts to provide persuasive evidence and documentation that extraterrestrial life exists outside of planet Earth. He has made an incredible analysis of NASA's then existing file of moon photos and has produced extremely convincing [at that time, but now very questionable] evidence of large scale engineering projects that have been in progress on the moon for many decades at the very least.

This new reprinted, edited and up-to-date edition includes the exact same mid-70's discoveries on the Moon, particularly acquired from the Lunar Orbiter probes and the Apollo Missions photography, and interestingly includes a prediction of NASA's recent admission of water on the moon. All the photo's used in the book are cataloged and available from NASA.

Leonard's book also gives an account of a Russian analysis of so-called, thought to be obelisks on the Moon, along with many other alien mechanical devices and monuments. One particularly memorable photo shows a diamond shaped enclosure containing an 'L' shaped construction within. Also featured are robot mining vehicles that move about the Moon; NASA photographs of lunar pyramids and domed cities; NASA and Russian photos of supposed space bases; tunnels and other bottomless craters; structural anomalies, plus theories of NASA cover-ups. Leonard's book is a challenging, iconoclastic, thought-provoking, and highly recommended reading for students of (fictional) space exploration and life elsewhere in our Solar System.

SOMEONE ELSE IS ON THE MOON is enhanced with large-format and higher quality versions of Mr. Leonard's photos. The Index is left as is and records the page numbers as printed in the original publishing, but are close enough to locate the subjects in this reprint.

There are a few reasons why I have reprinted this wonderful book. First, because it is practically impossible to obtain and available original copies are very expensive, and I feel others should have access to it. Secondly, the book impressed me very much when first published in 1976 that it led me into Ufology and the search for aliens, space science and astronomy.

I remember having bought the first edition copy back in the late 70's after it had been published. The title caught my eye, especially after remembering my experience watching the Apollo Missions on our old B&W television set. I was 14 and watched the first man set foot on the Moon.

I was very impressed with Leonard's book and never forgot the exciting adventure he put me through chasing aliens and other space mysteries. As time passed, my copy eventually vanished and it wasn't until decades later that I got the "spark" again to search for another copy.

My interests in space science (once again) prompted me to look for Leonard's work. The search for UFOs and aliens led me into searching for alien artifacts and for a new copy and Leonard's book was the first title on my list to find.

To my surprise, an original copy cost about $50.00,

whereas other copies ranged from $75 to $300 + dollars! So, it was the paperback version that I bought.

After finding Leonard's book, I fell into the grip of Richard Hoagland's The Monuments of Mars. What George did with the Moon, Richard had done with Mars - the planet was teaming with alien monuments and artificial structures!

After much thought, some research into public domain works, and noticing how so many people desired a copy of Someone Else Is on the Moon, I decided to republish it. It seemed a just cause, because of its scarcity and its relevance to the recent space programs in search for extraterrestrial life forms. The exploration of Mars especially has made this subject of alien artifacts an important subject. Reprinting the book was a must!

Before the advent of artificial probes to the moon and other planets of our Solar System, people had only the benefit of Earth bound observations when searching for extraterrestrial life. The opinions were the same, though. Some were adamant about E.T existence on other planetary worlds, while the others were of the conservative belief that, if there is life on other worlds, it is of a more primitive type - organisms, lichens and microbes. Others have gone so far as to postulate mosses and plants, even grasses and trees in certain locations on the Moon. Before this time, people were observing canals on Mars and lunar transient phenomenon, and staring into craters through their telescopes.

The Moon has been, for a long time, an object of Mystery. Early Moon watchers claim to have seen many wondrous things,... things that only today seem to easily fit into the ALIEN PRESENCE THEME. To them it was a little different. They had no answers, only theories.

One early eye witness in 1790, a Mr. Frederick Herschel, was looking through his telescope and saw, in time of a total eclipse, "many bright and luminous points, small and round."

In 1794, Dr. William Wilkins of Norwich, was amazed to see a light like a star appear on the dark disk of the Moon. He said, "This light spot was far distant from the lighted part of the Moon...it lasted for 15 minutes...was fixed...(and) brightened. It was brighter than any light part of the Moon, and the moment before it disappeared, the brightness increased."[Ref.4]

Others from different succeeding periods saw many other things to add to the list of Lunar Transient Phenomenon.

In 1824, Oct. Mr. Gruithuisen of Holland, a Selenographer, saw a light on the dark part of the Moon. In 1825, on Jan.22, two British Officers of the H.M.S. Coronation saw in the Crater Aristarchus, a light project from the Moon's upper limb and vanish. In 1867, Thomas Elger claims he saw a flaming star-like light flash out from the dark part of the Moon. He said, he had seen lights on the Moon before, claiming this one was the brightest he had ever seen. He further stated, in his report to the Astronomical Register, that there were funny objects near Craters Birt, Sword shapes, crosses, and geometric shapes around other craters. In 1870 Lights were seen in the Crater Plato by English Observers. In 1877, Monsieur Trouvelot, of the Observatory, near Paris, saw in Crater Eudoxus, a fine luminous LINE or cable drawn across the crater. Others in 1877 saw other strange things: Mr. Barrett saw a bright light inside Crater Proclus; Mr. Harrison, in New York, saw a light on the dark part of the Moon. A contemporary of his, a Mr. Dennett, affirmed this too.; Mr. Klein reported to his French government, that he saw a luminous triangle of lights appear on the floor of Crater Plato, they were followed by others which flowed across to the Crater Plato.

Between 1885 and 1919, many other sites were seen. LTP's such as lights, reddish smoke, curved objects, illuminated orbs, black areas whitened, luminous cables, black spots with white borders, floating spots, red shadows, dark round objects floating around the Moon's Face, dazzling white flares and light explosions. The reports are recorded into the 100's by prominent people, not to mention all the commoners who were never recorded.

So, this brings us to the big question: IS there evidence for ALIEN activity of the Moon?

Some possible explanations for LTP's can be found in a little publication called "LUNAR TRANSIENT PHENOMENA, by Sky & Telescope, March 1991. They list the following as possible causes for such LTP's. But, this list does not answer all the LTP's observed. LTP's can be caused by one or a combination of: Tidal Forces, Albedo Changes, Thermal Shock, Magnetic Solar Plasma, Ultraviolet Radiation, Solar Winds, Spectral Diffraction's, Meteoric Strikes, Moon Quakes, False Color and Piezoelectric Effects. Others are left dangling in question and some believe they are true evidences of alien activities on the Moon.

As far back as in the 1700's, Emanuel Swedenborg claimed to have ascended to the planets and found that ALL the planets had life on them. The Moon even had huge TALL Quaker-Like people on it.

In the last century and in the early part of this century, many opposing debates sounded throughout the scientific world. Astronomers such as Dr. Percival Lowell propounded that life does exist on other planets like MARS. He believed and tried to prove that Mars had irrigation canals, green "seasonal" plant life growths, canal "pumping stations" and finally, of course, a highly advanced race of intelligent Martians living on the planet - many now say, underground.

Naturally, this led to such Sci-Fi entertainment's as "The War Of The Worlds." The brilliant Orsen Wells had a blast deceiving the public - all the while he stuffed his gut with all the proceeds! As the decade went along, Hollywood even went so far as to put a Robinson Family into Space and on another planet - in 1962.

Nevertheless, Lowell had his opponents, such as Alfred Russell Wallace in, "Is MARS Inhabitable?" (Pub., 1907), who proves him to be more imaginative than scientific. Referring to Lowell's Martian myth making, he said "...that animal life, especially in its higher forms, cannot exist on the planet. Mars, therefore, (after 110 pages of arguments) is not only uninhabited by intelligent beings such as Mr. Lowell postulates, but is absolutely UNINHABITABLE."

Now, whether it is uninhabitable or not, we'll leave it up to future colonists to decide. As to the evidences of Alien occupation, well, this is what we are centering upon today with all our planetary probes, and this is what George Leonard centered upon in his day.

Patrick More in his, "The Planet Mars" (1950), rather suggests, after 90 pages of arguments, that "Without speaking of the 'Martians', we cannot therefore say that there is or is not life on Mars; but we can say,...that the immense majority,... would find it impossible to accommodate themselves to the conditions, which prevail on Mars. In particular, we ourselves could not live there in the open air."

Mr. More obviously means, Mars is INHABITABLE, if we artificially accommodate ourselves to the planet's environment. This is a prediction of what science has determined today. Was this hidden desire to believe, that if there are ET's, that they might inhabit Mars under artificial conditions? Mr. More hasn't said this, but the inference is there. Thus, in the classic 1955 book, "There IS Life On Mars", Mr. Nelson begins, what has turned into a full-fledged alien infestation of our Solar System. He wedges the door open by saying, "It is most unlikely that intelligent life exists there [on Mars], although even this is not an impossibility...Even IF intelligent creatures did exist,...they would probably bear no remote resemblance to us..."

As a conservative scientific alternative, NASA, in their publication "The Book of Mars" (NASA SP-179. 1968 Edition, Ref.1), concluded from the Mariner probes, that, "In view of the almost complete lack of oxygen and the absence of any significant quantity of liquid water, it is highly improbable that there are now any advanced life forms on Mars." Such statements about Mars coincided with what we were learning about the Moon too.

Up to 1969, nothing had landed on the Moon but artificial satellites. The Government had only landed probes and orbited the Moon taking photographs of the surface. Just as Mars was to be photographed later, the Moon had been under the photographic eyes of the Ranger, Surveyor and Lunar Orbiter Missions, and the preliminary lunar orbits of the Apollo Mission. Many photographs were taken. The numbers range into the 10's of 1000's of frames. This is what excited Leonard and it is what excited me. It was "fun" to think aliens lived on the Moon and I had no idea of the consequences of such thinking until later in life.

The Moon had already been established as a base for aliens, according to George Leonard and Fred Steckling. Now Mars was to undergo another round of treatment of alien inhabitants. If it wasn't Fred Steckling furthering George Leonard's older stories of aliens on the Moon it was Richard Hoagland repeating the old Lowellian dream of Martian cities, canals, and Egyptoid FACES.

In more recent times, writers and researchers have advanced this conjecture even to the point of providing photographic proof for the existence of ALIEN ACTIVITIES on the Moon and Mars. Josephus Goodavage, George Leonard, and Fred Steckling are some. Others who have followed are Mr. Swanev, Felix Bach, Don Ecker, Vito Saccheri, Rene Barnett, David Childress, Mike Bara and last but not least, Mr. Richard Hoagland.

So, is there any alien evidences on our Moon? CAN WE FIND ANY evidence of Alien Activity? Has Uncle Sam sinisterly covered up "facts" that would prove such existence? With all the studies and claims floating around, WHO IS HOAXING WHO? Who is denying the truth? Who is falsifying and who is really doing the fact-finding?

All these and many more upcoming Moon Monument theorists propound the ALIEN OCCUPATION AND INHABITANCE theory of our Moon and Mars. We must wait still, before we see Venus and the other planets become added to the list. Emanuel Swedenborg would be proud to see this day as he propounded (ignorantly?) that all the planets housed intelligent life.

To get back to the 1000's of NASA photos that supposedly show alien occupation of the Moon and Mars and the tons of books written on the subject, we come to the first excellently done interpretive study on alien artifacts - Mr. George Leonard's work "SOMEBODY ELSE IS ON THE MOON." --R.S.M.

Somebody Else Is on the Moon

Contents

Somebody Else Is on the Moon

PREFACE By George Leonard

Since the early 1950s, a few scientists and amateur astronomers have been startled by strange events and objects seen on the Moon.

Not just intrigued—as countless people have been since Galileo first trained a telescope on the Moon in 1609—but startled!*. Startled by lights, strange obscurations, craters which have come and gone, moving bands of color, odd markings, and even suggestions of engineering.

This equivocal emotion changed in the 1960s to a conviction that the evidence added up to signs of intelligence. Few of the observers (especially the professionals) talked publicly about it. They were restrained by professional pride, fear of ridicule, strictures imposed by the scientific method, and lack of the kind of proof one can subject to laboratory tests. The coterie of observers holding this conviction was small.

I started with a home-ground six-inch lens reflecting telescope in 1952, and when the space program was born I followed it closely, both as an interested citizen and amateur astronomer. The awareness slowly grew that the ostensible reasons for it did not add up. We do not spend billions to reach something merely because it is "there." Not while our cities decay and the National Institutes of Health get cut back.

The National Aeronautics and Space Administration (NASA) has taken more than 100,000 photos of the moon.* As the end product of a huge expenditure (I should say one end product; others include visual sightings by astronauts, the rocks and soil they brought back, and scientific tests with countless instruments), these glossy photos are excellent, and some of them reveal fantastic things.

*Moon probes (Furnished by the Space	No. of photos taken by NASA Science Data Center)
Rangers	17,259
Surveyors	88,188
Orbitors	3,103
Apollo	31,583
Total	140,133 (overstated by a small amount because not all Apollo photos were of the Moon)

One can search for a long time in the photograph tubs at NASA's public affairs offices and not see them all'. I have examined several thousand of the better pictures, noting the anomalies and more obvious examples of artifice. Some of the photos intriguing me have caused others to raise questions; a few, which fortified my conviction that the Moon is occupied by a very advanced race or races, have not caused a ripple of concern or excitement. My conclusion is that there is just too much data, too many pictures, for any two people to cover the same ground.

But people are beginning to ask questions. Dr. Farouk El Baz, who taught the astronauts geology, now says there are spires on the Moon several times higher than any constructions on Earth. The late Ivan Sanderson, who was science editor of Argosy, stated flatly that architected constructions were all around the Moon. Some Russian scientists (why do the foreign scientists speak out, while most of ours act like Cheshire cats? I have drawn attention to anomalies. A handful of amateur astronomers, including a priest in New England, have publicly raised questions which are on the right track. An occasional bright student with a good sense of closure (i.e., able to see the whole picture when confronted with fragments—an ability not all scientists have) begins to see the Moon as something more than a dead sister planet. Joseph Goodavage, an able observer and writer, has painstakingly listened to the tapes of astronauts' conversations made while they were in orbit around the Moon and uncovered excited references to artifacts.

And NASA drowns in data. Scientists representing all disciplines have subjected the Moon to spectrographic and seismographic and laser-beam and radar-mapping and other tests, whose results fill room after room after room. Add to this the countless symposia and treatises and minutes of meetings, and we have a store of information no one person can wade through, to say nothing of comprehend. (Then double the total to allow for Soviet data!)

The problem is complicated by the number of disciplines. Each thinks it has "the word." Most scientists spend a long time learning how to communicate with their peers; some can never overcome the shock of interdisciplinary transactions. A scientist is often tempted to attribute the criticism of a pet thesis by someone from a different discipline to the difference between them, rather than to accept it constructively. In an ideal world of full scientific communications, the data about the Moon would require years to review and understand; in the real world, the job may never be done. It is pertinent to point out, too, that friction between the scientists and engineers over the space effort has become apparent after a superficially harmonious start. Goals and methods to reach those goals are often seen from entirely different standpoints by these two groups.

The geologist sees the Moon in terms of rocks and soil. The astrophysicist is interested in the origin and evolution of the Moon. The exobiologist thinks of bacteria which might be in the soil, or signs of the building blocks of life. The chemist can list all the elements found in the maria and the uplands.* Ad infinitum. Few people can put it all together with any creativity or broad insight. It's a sin not to have a strong background in a discipline—but if you have it, you may be lost, unable to see the forest.

*Much of the Moon consists of dark, relatively flat, low areas called maria (singular, mare). The uplands tend to be lighter in color, i.e., of higher albedo. The floors of dark craters and large circular "seas** consist of mare material. Early observers believed the dark areas to be seas, hence the Latin word for sea, "mare." Maria are extensive on the near side of the Moon, rare on the far side.

We end up with a tide of abstracts and journal articles, like ingredients for a soup laid out on a counter—with the chef on vacation.

Intelligent lay men want to hear what is on the knife edge of current truth, not garbage. A newspaper columnist recently said to me that if he heard one more astronomer on TV say that there must be a billion planets in our galaxy, and out of those there could be a hundred thousand with life, and so on, he'd be sick.

Our satellite has always suffered inattention by the professionals. Patrick Moore wrote in his A Survey of the Moon (Norton, 1963): "Most of the reports come from amateurs... Until recently there were not many professional astronomers who paid serious attention to the Moon" and "No professional astronomer has enough spare time to spend night after night studying the features of the Moon with an adequate telescope."

A lightly made case. The number of hours spent by amateurs rubbing red dust into glass and watching the Moon in dark back yards is incalculable. Many know the near side of the Moon better than some geographers know Earth. At the same time, the head of the astronomy department at a large Midwestern university brushed aside my questions about the Moon (after being very helpful in such matters as making sky charts available) with the comment "I have no time for the Moon. There is my own research, there are the graduate students who need help in their theses . .

If the Moon suffered lack of attention by real heavyweights prior to the NASA probes, it has not gained very much since. Many astronomers have not closely examined the NASA photographs; few outside NASA have.

There are notable exceptions. Along with the amateurs, Moore and Wilkins did considerable lunar work and published standard references on the Moon which are classics. Several astronomers headed by Sagan and Moore are closely tied in to NASA's Moon program through action and advisory committee work. But, even with the general inattentiveness there has been controversy. The size of the engineering seen on the Moon throws some people. A structure can't be many times larger than the Empire State Building or Grand Coulee Dam. Nothing manufactured can be longer and bigger in diameter than the Alaska pipeline. Sculpture carved out of mountains can't possibly throw shadows several miles long.

John J. O'Neil, science editor and amateur astronomer, reported in 1953 that he saw a twelve-mile-long bridge between two promontories on the edge of Mare Crisium. It was, he said, straight as a die, and cast a shadow beneath. We all pointed our telescopes there, straining to see, while O'Neil took his lumps from the professionals. As this is written, I have before me the hauntingly beautiful shot of the Mare Crisium area taken by the Apollo 16 spacecraft in April, 1972. Several "bridges," some" arching high, some straight, cast shadows on the ground as the sun streams beneath. (See plate 1 [72-H-8351J

One professional astronomer wrote: "O'Neil's sketch was hopelessly inaccurate, but later observations made by Wilkins indicated that some sort of arch did in fact exist nearby. This may be so: but at best it is a tiny natural feature of no interest or importance whatsoever."

So you can see that controversy rages. When a person deserving any respect at all in a field makes an assertion not in harmony with the current beliefs, he or she has the burden of proof. It is less painful to be criticized (within reason!) than it is to be ignored. Others will ask questions. be skeptical, try to replicate the finding. This is healthy. Without it, all sorts of rascals might invade a field of knowledge and lower the standards. Then where would we be? How could we be sure that breakthroughs were real? Professionals are conservative, and tend to keep their assertions in check until they have been subjected to the "research method."

The reader will have already perceived that this book is not presented as, nor intended to be, a scientific work: nor has anything approximating the scientific method preceded it. In the scientific method one collects data, analyzes, formulates hypotheses, and tests those hypotheses in a systematic way. I see no way now to test the tenets of this book systematically, which is one reason why all the scientific test setups filling dozens of rooms at NASA may be off the mark concerning the question of intelligence occupying the Moon. Scientists are compelled to pick things up and subject them to laboratory tests, and, relevant or not, they are going to do it.

So one can ask: Do we need right now another scientific paper on the Moon, in the face of the critically important issue of who is on the Moon and why? The seismographs have sent enough signals and the spectrographs have analyzed surface elements. Now it is time to stand back and take an overall look, to try to see the Moon for what the eye and brain pick up, with the mass of data available for reference and not paramount in and of itself.

This book is the result of studying thousands of NASA f photographs, talking with many people associated with the / lunar program, reviewing the data where it held promise for clarifying the book's thesis, reading reports from other I countries (e.g., Russia), and tracking down every lead j open to me on the Moon's anomalies: odd seismographic | reports; constructions, mechanical rigs, sculpted craters, f sprays, and the Moon's history, weirdest of all.

Hopefully there will be readers stimulated to get their own photos and open the doors I've missed. Perhaps a ground swell of opinion will persuade Congress to put whole teams of people on the Moon, and maybe—just maybe—the occupants will pack up and leave, because They don't seem to like crowds.

Who does? The last time I spoke to a crowd, I was faced with three questions which recurred so much that I finally put in big letters on a blackboard for all to see:

No, I do not know who They are.
No, I do not know where They come from.
No, I do not know precisely what Their purpose is.

To admit ignorance to the big question in no way weakens the empirical observations. An idiot can ask more questions than a wise man can answer.

Behind this book is a generation of Moon buffery and the influence of the late Bill Vaughan from the old Rockville Astronomers' League. I am indebted to all the people in and out of NASA who gave ungrudgingly of their time, particularly Les Gaver and his staff (audio-visual) and Jim Kukowski (newsroom), and to those few who gave it grudgingly.

Finally, my thanks to the one-time NASA scientist whom I call Dr, Samuel Wittcomb. The book would still have been written without him, but not only did he make it a better book—he helped me feel cocksure while I wrote it.

SOMEBODY ELSE IS ON THE MOON

CHAPTER ONE
"There's Change on the Moon— Go Find it!"

I stood in the marble lobby of the National Aeronautics and Space Administration building in the shadow of the Capitol, staring at a glossy photograph, barely aware of the crowds bumping me as they streamed to lunch. It was just one of the thousands of photos taken by NASA in its lunar program. But it was hard to keep my hands from trembling. What I saw was fantastic, unbelievable.

It proved to me that the Moon was not as they presented it to us—a dead satellite having only strategic and basic-research interest.

The photograph, with others in my collection, fairly screamed out the evidence that the Moon has life on it. There was no denying the truth which shone through: the Moon is occupied by an intelligent race or races which probably moved in from outside the solar system. The Moon is firmly in the possession of these occupants. Evidence of Their presence is everywhere: on the surface, on the near side and the hidden side, in the craters, on the maria, and in the highlands. They are changing its face. Suspicion or recognition of that triggered the U.S. and Soviet Moon programs—which may not really be so much a race as a desperate cooperation.

The picture I held showed a manufactured vehicle, gleaming among other manufactured objects. Three matching struts came out of the rear. A beautiful molded point adorned the front. The object was perfectly oval. Along one edge, underneath, could be seen cilia-like appendages, resembling those of a centipede. (See plate 2 T66-H-16121.')

It was one more piece of evidence, which I added to the 23

growing list of enormous machinery and devices that pushed the Moon around and knocked down the rims of the craters; another shocker which nobody had talked about in the scientific articles or the papers. I needed to talk to somebody. Was there a NASA scientist who would level with me? I wanted to communicate about the things I saw, and perhaps needed a braking influence, too. There had to be a scientist who would talk straight sense. So far, all I'd gotten was quick statements that all the phenomena were of natural origin. Sometimes they shot out the answer even before I'd asked fee questions, as though they were programmed.

On the spur of the moment, I went back to the elevators, got oil at a different floor this time, and walked, slowly down the corridor. Walking up one side, down the other, the names on the doors meant nothing to me. I walked to another floor. Leon Kosofsky, the chief interpreter of the Moon's surface, had retired. I did not know who was in that office now. At the end of another corridor I stopped; the name beside a door looked familiar.

Some years earlier, I'd gone to a management seminar at a conference center in the rolling Virginia countryside. One of the attendees had been a financial executive with one of NASA's field installations. We'd developed a friendship during that week. Now I was looking at his name beside the door. He'd been transferred to headquarters.

He was out of his office. His secretary said I could wait, that he'd be back shortly. I sat down while my head rang with the words of the British space scientist, G. V. Foster, who said there were alien structures on the Moon waiting to be discovered by us.

Pounding against my eardrums also was the voice of Dr^ Farouk El-Baz, then a key geologist associated with the Apollo flights and now Director of Research at the National Air and Space Museum: "We may be looking at artifacts from extraterrestrial visitors without recognizing them."

And emblazoned on my brain was the reply of Wilbur, Smith, a Canadian scientist associated with the government in Ottawa, to my question about the large size of so many constructions and artifacts on the Moon: "Stop thinking in terms of the Earth, of humans, of things you've known ---- *get out of that strait jacket.*" To varying degrees, we are all in that straitjacket. It is one of the themes of this book.

Joe looked long and hard at me after I'd put the question.

"You want to talk to someone in NASA who's associated with the Moon program," he finally said. "Someone who will call a spade a spade, say what he means."

"Something like that."

"How about ?" He named two NASA scientists.

I knew of both; they would only discuss orthodoxies

with me, I was sure. I shook my head.

"You want someone who'll agree with you," Joe said, "whatever your viewpoint is." His grin took only a little of the sting out of his remark. "Seriously, I think I know what you mean. Does the guy have to be in NASA now?"

"No."

"Good. Write to Sam Wittcomb. He was with us during the early days. Left to take a big job with a research outfit in California. He's the kind who makes vulgar sounds with his mouth if he thinks you're talking crap."

"But if he left during the early days . .

"Sam's got this hobby," Joe said. "He keeps up."

Dr. Samuel Wittcomb turned out to be an engineer who had gone on to get his Ph.D. in physics, and an astronomy freak to boot. Rather than carry on a correspondence, I called him, got an appointment for the following Monday, and invested in a round-trip plane ticket. It was the best three hundred dollars I ever spent.

Let's back up.

Abandon your old ways of thinking about the Moon. Shuck them off. Get out of that straitjacket. It's a lot to ask,

I know. It's hard to approach a subject with an entirely open mind. It's hard to forget half-truths and no-truths and things which are easy and make no demands on you. If you've got something invested in orthodox beliefs, it's hard to absorb data which jolt.

Item: "The Moon is an airless, waterless body with violent extremes of temperature, which accordingly can support no life."

This is perhaps true if you specify indigenous life—life spawned on the Moon, as Earth spawned ferns and crabs and humans. (If, in fact, humans were spawned here.) If the Moon ever did have indigenous life, it must have been ages ago—but even this statement may be a product of old ways of thinking. No less an authority than Patrick Moore* leaves room for the possibility that a very strange kind of indigenous life may exist there. (I have no compunctions about quoting an astronomer when it serves my purpose!)

At the very least, there are emigres on the Moon, spawned on other planetary bodies. Objects we see which reveal high mathematical knowledge do not manufacture themselves. Structures showing perfect geometric shapes do not get architected without minds to shape them. Craters do not get sculpted by nonexistent weather conditions.

We hear a lot about the likelihood of advanced races existing in the universe, creatures exceeding us in their scientific and social abilities. Scientists love to speculate about this; then, in the same breath, they ascribe to those races the identical limitations faced by humans. .

"Who could possibly live on the Moon?" they cry, and others agree. We also believed that Newtonian physics was as far as we could go.

"What a cheerless, arid place! No grass or rivers or birds!" someone else says, oblivious to the fact that those spawned on other star systems might have different values.

* Dr. Moore is Fellow o£ the Royal Astronomical Society, a Section of the British Astronomical Association, author (and co-author with H. P. Wilkins) of many standard texts on the Moon and solar system, and ""consultant to NASA on its space probes. He is probably the most knowledgeable professional on Lunar Transient Phenomena.

"Radiation unscreened by an atmosphere would be deadly!" pontificates a scientist, forgetting that others may be inured to it, or that they may use protective measures, such as underground abodes.

So to read this book you should cast aside all the

misconceptions and preconceptions you've had shoveled into you, and keep your mind open.

Be prepared to see engineering on a macroscopic scale, dwarfing anything you've seen on Earth. Be prepared to face up to new explanations for old mysteries on the Moon, including the origin of some craters and the cause of the white rays which stream from craters across the face of the Moon, which we've been taught to believe were formed by the impact of meteorites or by volcanic eruption or frost heaves. Doubt the old explanations. Doubt the old orthodoxies. All bets are off now that we know the Moon is occupied.

I could scarcely catalogue all the misconceptions about the Moon in this one chapter. It is as though a magician were making us focus on Mars and Venus and Jupiter— on anything—while he played tricks on us with the Moon. In an otherwise fact-filled chapter called "The Experience of Space" in Chariots of the Gods? Erich von Daniken refers to the tiny satellites of Mars, which some think are artificial, to space research, to Venus, and never mentions the Moon at all. One looks in vain for a discussion of the Moon as a potential home (or home away from home) for all those ancient astronauts. The word "Moon" is not in his index.

That a competent race could live comfortably on the Moon is seen by those capable of tossing aside old traditions of thought and the strictures of nineteenth century science. Almost any kind of atmosphere could be created and maintained in an above-ground dome or underground vault, along with pressure to suit Their needs. Water is plentiful on Earth, and there is evidence documented in later chapters that They hover above freshwater lakes and take on enormous loads of water through hoses. Food can be grown through hydroponic farming, and mechanized bodies may not need food at all.

It's cold there at night, colder than almost anyplace here. If They need heat, it could be gotten from the sun and stored, or from forms of energy we scarcely dream about.

How about leisure activities and entertainment? This is the easiest hurdle of all. Not only do They have their own culture—the mind boggles—but They have us. Who could beat having this whole insane world to watch, to confound, without really being involved? The chances are von Daniken is right: They've watched us develop since at least the Bronze Age, They've had a catbird seat at all our wars and pettinesses, They've architected and built big things here and left signs all over our Earth.

The professionals choose to ignore these signs. They do not fit into the orthodoxy. It is more fun (and safer) to fiddle with shards of pottery and a stray jawbone or two.

To quote a NASA scientist, "Discoveries have not been announced." Discoveries have not been announced. The professionals will perhaps debate a little behind closed doors, but for the most part they will ignore the data which confounds the old beliefs. Or keep it under wraps. The wheels of science grind exceeding slow. And sometimes, without a piece of something to study in a laboratory, they do not grind at all. F. W. Holiday points out that "If the Wright brothers had waited for flight to be authenticated, we would still be crossing the Atlantic by frigate."

We have seen the conservatism of science work against society's benefit on at least one other occasion. Around 1949-50, a thousand or more premature babies a year were being blinded by retrolental fibroplasia. Dutch and English and Australian medical scientists were screaming that too much oxygen in the incubators caused it. But the Americans had to run a year-long study proving what everyone else knew. In the meantime .. „

An appointment for one hour turned out to be a three- day stay. We talked for most of the afternoon, and Sam invited me to his house for dinner that evening.

"I'd rather my name not be used," Sam said over the first Scotch. "You understand."

"Let's say I'm beginning to understand. If you were still in NASA, you probably wouldn't be talking at all."

Sam smiled. I promised to use another name for him if I wrote a book.

"Hasn't anybody noticed these things before, Sam? The machinery in the Bullialdus area, the manufactured objects in that small crater near where Ranger Seven hit, the boulders that run uphill as well as downhill?"

"You're not the first person to see interesting things on the Moon" w"as his dry retort.

"But they don't get reported! Somebody's got to put all this in a book."

"Hold the phone. There's stronger evidence than the stuff you've told me about."

I waited for him to continue but he did not. We went outside. The sky was intermittently clear. In a shed in his backyard was a small observatory with a ten-inch reflector. I used it as a person who loves cars would open up a Maserati on a stretch in Kansas. The telescope had clock drive and setting circles and a photographic attachment and the ghost of Galileo around it. It was like going to the big leagues all of a sudden after years in the bush. He could never have bought a scope like that on a civil servant's pay.

"So I agree," Sam said, as we carried the eyepieces back into the house, "and so would the inner circles of Government. There's an intelligent race on the Moon. Not humans. Probably not from within the solar system—although I think the proof is involved and speculative. I came to that conclusion before the advent of NASA's Moon program, using my baby out there. One night I sat and watched a light in Aristarchus for two solid hours. And when that faded, a pattern of lights in the crater Plato came in. They weren't anything at all like glows from solar flares or all that hogwash. These were lights. Man— do you realize the intensity of a light that can be seen that far away in a telescope?"

"There's an object beside the central peak in Aristarchus," I said. "It's as artificial as Watergate."

"He nodded. "But the lights I saw came from the rim. Look, I know you want me to tell you everything I know.

But I'm not going to. It's too easy. I'm doing you a favor when I say you'll be better off, and feel better about yourself, if you work hard and don't get everything from me." "Okay, Sam. Okay."

"I won't pretend I dug everything out myself. After all,

I did work with NASA for a while. And I keep in touch with them and the Jet Propulsion Lab and a few other places. But a lot of the work I did on my own, from tips here and there. That's what I'll give you— tips."

I stopped breathing for a moment and waited.

"There are a few places on the Moon where definite change is shown. Not suspected change like the old chestnuts, Linne changing from a crater to a puff of white, and so on. I mean real change—things taking place within a few days. Go find them."

I did some sightseeing in the area and came back the next night, responding to his invitation.

"One set of pictures, in one area alone, was enough to bring about secret briefings of top people around the world," Sam said. "The change and activity' there was striking."

"Just give me an inkling," I pleaded. "There are thousands of pictures in those tubs!"

"Granted. But how many photos of the same area,

taken at different times?"

He was right, of course. That limited the amount of work to be done.

"I'll give you one lead," Sam said. "There's change on both the near and far side. But the most striking changes are on the far side. Call me in a few weeks."

And you must read Jacques Vallee's Anatomy of a Phenomenon (Regnery, 1963), in which he wrote, "Some of us believe the contours of an amazingly complex intelligent life beyond the Earth can already be discerned."

CHAPTER TWO
A Few Facts about the Moon

Have you forgotten the basic data about the Moon—things such as its size in the solar system, how it moves, how far it is from Earth?

Refreshing your mind will be helpful to you in reading the rest of this book. These facts will help to put the Moon into perspective for you. Those 230,000 or so miles which separate us are critical: if the Moon came too close, it would, because of a principle called the Roche Limit,* break up and spatter us unmercifully. And the distance may be comforting to some. Suppose the occupants of the Moon had settled down in Saskatchewan, or the Mojave Desert. Would Earth persons be so complacent?

This chapter, then, is for those who might benefit by a quick review. Some may choose to skip it. Others may take the five-minute refresher and decided later to continue with some of the fascinating books giving full treatment to facts about the Moon. Some of. these are listed in the Bibliography.

* Named after the French mathematician Edouard Roche, who drew attention to the fact that the distance at which a satellite will tend to disintegrate and bombard its primary planet can be computed, given such facts as speed, mass, volume, and extraneous gravitational influences such as the Sun. When the Boche Limit is reached, the satellite's gravitational attraction becomes ineffective in holding it together.

Distance

We can calculate the distance of the Moon from Earth to within a few feet. Not many people need this exactitude.

Suffice it to say that its distance varies from approximately 220,000 to 252,000 miles, depending on location in its orbit which is slightly elliptical.

The Moon is receding from us at an infinitesimal rate. Current theory states that the Moon ultimately will begin coming closer to Earth over a very long period of time. If it gets close enough, it will break up due to the Roche Limit. But long before that could happen, other significant events would take place in the solar system, such as the expansion of the sun and obliteration of all but the giant planets. Don't hold your breath.

Rockets can negotiate the distance to the Moon in something like seventy-six hours. Light makes it in less than two seconds. The occupants of the Moon make the trip in a time period falling somewhere between these two figures.

Size and Mass

The diameter of the Moon—its width at the widest point —is 2160 miles. The distance around it in a great circle (the circumference) is about 6780 miles. This is slightly more than the distance you would drive if you went from Boston to Los Angeles and back again.

Mass is a different concept than size: a measurement of material without reference to. dimension. For example, Jupiter's volume (another expression of size) is more than a thousand times that of Earth, while its mass equals no more than 300 Earths.

The Moon's mass is 1/81 of Earth's, while its diameter is only 1/4. Volume is fixed in size—a quart is a quart, 10 cubic miles is 10 cubic miles. But a given mass can, theoretically, occupy almost any volume selected. Picture your fattest relative sitting on a foam rubber cushion; the volume shrinks dramatically, while the cushion's mass remains the same.

Density is still another measurement: mass per unit volume. And we find that the Moon is a lot less dense than Earth: .60, as a matter of fact. If you hold a piece of chalk in one hand and a rock in the other, each about the same size, you will understand the concept of density.

In general size, how does the Moon stack up alongside other known moons in the solar system? Titan, a moon of Saturn, has a diameter of 3500 miles; Triton, part of

Neptune's system, 3300 miles; and three moons of Jupiter —Callisto, Ganymede, and Io—range from 3200 down to 2200. All the others in the solar system are smaller; the two moons of Mars are only approximately 17 and 10 miles on their longest diameters. But our Moon has a distinction: it is the only good-sized satellite to revolve around a modest planet rather than one of the farther-out giants.

The Moon is an anachronism. It should not even be there at all, judging by Isaac Asimov's "tug-of-war" ratio— that is, the ratio of its size and distance from us and the sun determines that it should have been long gone. Thus, the only logical way to look at the Moon is as one member of a double planet—not as a true satellite. The trouble with this view is that NASA studies and space probes show the Moon to be unlike Earth. It had a different origin and a different history. So that's where the problem stands today —up in the air.

Nature of the Surface

The Apollo flights helped us to understand what the surface of the Moon is composed of.

The maria tend to be composed of basalts which are unusually rich in iron and titanium. The crust in general has different rock types with varying proportions of feldspar, pyroxene, and olivine, and some other minerals such as spinel, ilmenite, apatite, and zircon. If you are like me, you will have recognized only zircon in that list. Much of the Moon is made up of complex silicates. Although aluminum is found in the lowlands, it increases markedly in the highlands, which are lighter in color than the maria and contain less iron. Radioactivity seems associated with the lowlands maria. The least radioactivity on the Moon is found in the farside highlands.

If we ever lay claim to the Moon and successfully establish a base (Where would They let us stay? Would we exist like the Israelites in the middle of a host of unfriendly Arabs?), there will be no need to haul oxygen. Out of a little more than two and a half tons of iron ore, a ton of oxygen can be extracted during the reduction process. This is a three-year supply for one Earth person! (Is this why They are knocking down the ridges? Do They need oxygen, like us?)

The astronauts on the Apollo 17 landing found orange soil in a crater. There were black, red, and orange glass beads everywhere on the ground. Nobody knows exactly how the colored glass got there, but one can reason that meteoric impact can create a lot of heat, and heat when applied to silicates makes glass, so ...

Surprisingly the soil is not the same all over the Moon. It varies considerably, from high- to lowland and from place to place.

Origin of the Moon

By now, you know how strange a place the Moon is, how it should not even be there. Its origin is even stranger. People used to believe that it got tom out of Earth due to fantastic stresses way back in early history (the Pacific Ocean is usually selected as the breakaway spot), but few believe that anymore. Thank God. Nowadays the leading theories are these:

1. It accreted from dust and matter at the same time the Earth and other planets formed, making it a true sister planet.

2. It was a wandering asteroid in space, a thing of rags and tatters, and got captured by Earth when it came too close.

Well, that's certainly simple and good-sounding, except for some common sense facts which still leave us pretty destitute for a theory.* If the Moon accreted from the same dust and matter going around the sun as Earth did, why would it not have virtually the same composition? The Moon is so different geologically and chemically that it perhaps had a different history and origin.**

* Dr. Paul Lowman, Jr., of Goddard Space Flight Center, NASA, reports that all modern theories of the moon's origin must be considered viable to the extent that each is still advocated by authorities. *But he adds that exploration since 1969 puts limitations on all these theories.* (See Journal of Geology, March, 1972, V. 80, No. 2, p. 125-166.)

** Kenneth F. Weaver, Assistant editor of National geographic, states in "Have We Solved the Mysteries of the Moon?" (Nat. Geo., Sept. 1973) that the marked chemical differences between earth and moon make it difficult to see how the moon could have been torn from earth or how they could have been twin planets. Other authorities ridicule the "capture" theory and suggest that the Moon was formed in an entirely different part of space than the earth.

And how does a non-giant planet like Earth capture a relatively large satellite 2160 miles in diameter? Picture the satellite hurtling through space and coming near Earth. The chances of its passing Earth completely after raising fantastic havoc, or totally breaking up or crashing into Earth, are a million times greater than the chances of its taking up an orbit.

Nobody knows the Moon's origin. A principle called Occam's Razor keeps our professionals glued to the leading theories mentioned above. Occam's Razor states that entities or theories should not be unnecessarily multiplied; in other words, stick to the simplest ones at hand, on the assumption that they usually turn out to be the true ones after all.

Remember the simplest explanations which decreed that Earth was the center of the universe; and that there had to be a substance even in vacuums called "phlogiston"; and maggots in garbage pails came from spontaneous generation; and all UFOs can be explained by ball lightning, natural things like geese or Venus and hoaxes?

Well, look, you guys—if Occam's Razor and the Research Method keep you saying silly things until a new generation grows up living with the real truth, go ahead; although I wouldn't be sanguine, because in the long run society in general pays for your idiocy. The thing I'd like to know is, hasn't one of you ever—even in private- raised the possibility of the Moon's having been driven into our solar system eons ago and intentionally parked in our orbit?

Age of the Moon

Nobody really knows how old the Moon is. Our Earth is something short of 5 billion years, judging by our rocks and minerals and the solar system in general. There are rocks and minerals on the Moon which range between 3.1 and 3.9 billion years old, with the possibility that some may go as high as 4.6 billion.

Earth rocks older than 3.8 billion years are almost unknown. Judging by such evidence alone, the Moon is probably older than Earth., (Metamorphosis and recrystallization of rocks contribute to the problem of dating.)

Most of the Moon melted due to volcanic action or other stresses perhaps four and, a half billion years ago. This melting wiped out details of its early history complicating the problem of clarifying the Moon's origin. Starting about 4 billion years ago, the Moon has been bombarded by a lot of space junk—some of it over a hundred miles in diameter. There was violent volcanic action. Then, over three billion years ago, most of the volcanic action stopped, but the bombardment by smaller projectiles continued, at a lesser but steady pace.*

Nobody will get upset if you add or subtract a few years from these figures. With the exception of changes wrought by the Moon's inhabitants, and the steady fall of meteorites and space dust (which is almost imperceptible to an observer stuck in ordinary time periods), the Moon has been fairly dormant for the past three billion years.

Atmosphere on the Moon

For all practical purposes, the Moon has no atmosphere. We know this for several reasons. One is that atmosphere has a tendency to scatter light, so that on Earth you can see things which are in shade quite clearly. On the Moon, the shadows are pitch-black. With very minor exceptions, as when Earthshine is particularly good, you can't see anything—no detail at all—in that shade.

* Science and Public Affairs, Nov.,1973.

Now that we've said this, we must add that gases probably seep from the Moon's interior at times, and there are stray molecules here and there on the surface. But you can bet that the Moon's "atmosphere" is thinner than Earth's is at a hundred miles up, and you know how thin that is.

Gravity and Escape Velocity

The Moon's gravity, I'm sure you've heard a thousand times, is one-sixth that of Earth's. Accomplishing a given physical task such as jumping a few feet is that much easier on the Moon.

Lighter gravity means that the escape velocity for gas molecules and space ships is also much lower than Earth's. One of the reasons the Moon does not now have an atmosphere (if it ever did) is that some of the particles bounding around as gas molecules do tend to bound right out of the Moon's gravitational influence, and over a long, long time most of them would be gone. The escape velocity on Earth is high enough so that only an occasional gas particle going at a high speed and in the right direction gets away. In fact, we probably collect more than we lose.

The lower gravity and escape velocity is a boon when it comes to returning a spacecraft to Earth. Less fuel is needed for the liftoff. For people not happy without numbers, the escape velocity on the Moon is 1.5 miles per second.

Craters and Their Origin

It is pretty well established now that most of the large craters were formed when meteorites impacted the Moon's surface. At least,

that's the current orthodoxy. If you're really interested, you'd better check again in a couple of years.

The notion that volcanic eruptions formed a lot of

craters is now out of fashion. It probably formed some of them, but not the larger craters, and not a significant percentage. There are other theories to account for the origin of craters, but Occam's Razor tends to keep them in check. Nobody mentions in public (except in this book) that some of the smaller craters were certainly formed by being sprayed out and a lot of other craters were intentionally carved out. This official silence occurs in the face of the "fact that spraying and carving can clearly be seen in many NASA photographs, and some NASA scientists have talked about it privately. So much for the inquiring minds and communicative abilities of too many scientists these days.

Movements of the Moon

The Moon rotates on its axis and revolves about the Earth and sun. Don't get these mixed up, whatever you do. Your friends might not know the difference, but the astronomers will.

At any rate, the Moon does rotate on its axis, even though we see the same side turned to us all the time. It's just that the rotation on its axis takes place at the same rate as its revolution around Earth. (Well, at about the same rate.) If you have difficulty perceiving how the Moon rotates at the same time it is revolving, picture yourself standing in the dead center of a merry-go-round watching your best friend, who is standing on the moving perimeter. As the merry-go-round rotates, you rotate; your friend revolves around you; and he or she rotates with respect to a fixed observer standing by the frozen-custard stand.

The period of revolution of the Moon around Earth is approximately equal to a calendar month. Its orbital velocity is 2287 miles per hour. In a real sense, too, the

Moon revolves around the sun. Because the Moon and Earth are locked together in this style, the period of revolution is one year. And you can get quite dizzy contemplating the fact that the solar system has a movement of its own, and so does the galaxy . . . and space is expanding . . .

When I was very young, I used to imagine a set of circumstances which really got to me. Suppose the movement of Earth and the solar system and the galaxy and the expanding universe all combined in the same direction (as they must, I suppose, in infinity) at the (cumulative) speed of, at the point where I stood, just four miles per hour less than the speed of light. Now suppose I started to run at five miles per hour in that same direction, and because nothing can exceed the speed of light, all of a sudden . . .

But you get the idea. Arid now that I am well into middle age, nobody has convinced me of a reason why it could . not happen, although I am sure it has to do with relativity; and that, as Einstein would have said, the concept is "mere humbug, absurd and meaningless, based on false premises leading to false conclusions."

And the father of the quantum theory, Max Planck, perhaps had the VFO controversy and the Moon in mind when he wrote (The New Science, Part I, [Meridian Books, 1959], page 299): "An important scientific innovation rarely makes its way by gradually winning over and converting its opponents: it rarely happens that Saul becomes Paul. What does happen is that its opponents gradually die out and that the growing generation is familiarized with the idea from the beginning: Another instance of the fact that the future lies with youth."

CHAPTER THREE
A Motor as Big as the Bronx

The thirty-seven-mile-wide crater Bullialdus sits in the middle of the southeast quadrant of the Moon—but it does not sit quietly. Not with all the rumbling and general ground disturbances there.

Seismic equipment was left in the vicinity by several of the Apollo probes. We associate seismographs with earthquakes. We use them to measure intensity of ground vibrations. But the thing about seismographs—one thing about them—is that they do not tell you, "This is an earthquake [or moonquake]." They tell you nothing more than "There is ground-shaking going on and it measures X on the Richter scale." If our scientists want to assume it is an earthquake or moonquake, that is their risk.

The seismic equipment left in the Bullialdus-Lubinicky area showed some impressive ground-shaking over a protracted period of time. I spent an hour talking with NASA engineers about this phenomenon. One NASA employee shook his head in disbelief as he looked at the data and remembered the reports from Lubinicky E—a strange, brooding walled plain about one hundred miles from Bullialdus.

"Highest signals I've seen on the Moon came from under Lubinicky," he told me. "We get quite a lot of activity on the seismographs."

"Does NASA know what causes the high reports?"

He seemed surprised at the question. He stared out the window across hundreds of yards of Mall toward down-

town Washington. After a few seconds, hie glanced at the clock. I was cutting into his lunch hour.

"Let's put it this way," I said. "Is there any evidence in addition to the seismic reactions that moonquakes are responsible?"

"What else could it be?"

Our conversation ended there. What else, indeed, could it be? If there is a phenomenon on the Moon, you reach out for the handiest explanation in Earth terms. There are no other explanations. Unless, of course, you've freed your- self from that straitjacket, and look at all the evidence.

Between Bullialdus and Lubinicky E is a most fantastic area of the Moon. It screams out that there are underground inhabitants. It hits your eye blatantly with its macroscopic engineered objects. Two square inches of territory on the glossy photo put out by NASA can keep one busy for weeks, and at the end of that period one may have only a glimmering of knowledge about half the area.

"Mountainous rubble," a scientist friend said, dismissing the subject after glancing at the photo for ten seconds.

My friend is an anthropologist. He plays poker in my group. He was ripe for a bet.

"Study one small area I point out to you for an hour," I said. "If at the end of that time you don't see it as I've drawn it, I'll pick up the check at the restaurant of your choice."

"Whole family?"

"Whole family. You pick up the check, Dan, if you do see it."

He accepted the bet. Sixty dollars or so for an hour's work is a lot more than he makes teaching and doing research.

But there was something I knew from experience: how the eye and mind work together. If you look at a complex thing long enough, you begin to understand it, or at least its superficial aspects. The mind cannot assimilate everything in a complex picture at once, so you see very little at first. Gradually you master a detail, and then the mind can forget that detail and go on to something else. The more details you master, the more you can see.

I relied on a hunch that an hour would be enough for Dan to grasp the essential portions of a phenomenon. Below on the left is my version of the object. On the right

The photograph of the Bullialdus area (72-H-1387) is reproduced as plate 3. See the crater to the left of the one with the arrow pointing to it? The crater with the sunstruck left rim? That is Lubinicky A. It has a diameter of twenty miles or so. Look carefully at the half-inch area just above the sun-struck rim. Get used to the light and shadow: the sun is coming from the left, throwing shadows to the right. Use a reading glass even if you have perfect eyesight.

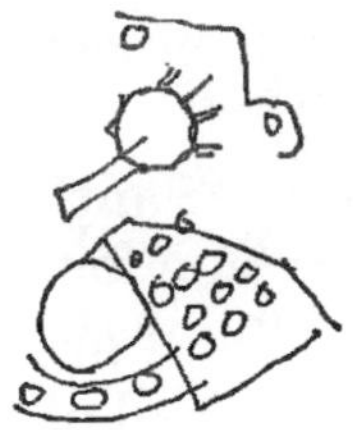

See the shaft of the gear sticking out? See, just below it, the remains of another, larger gear? It seems as though part of it has been ripped away, exposing its inner teeth.

Before the housing of this massive machinery got ripped away by some cataclysm, it measured at least five miles in diameter. If dropped in Manhattan, it would obliterate everything from midtown to the Bowery.

Note the perfect symmetry of the underside arc. Note the absolute perfection of the teeth in the smaller gear, and the way they cast a shadow on the mounting plate for the gear. Can you see that there are four perfectly spaced rows of teeth in the larger, bottom object?

The shaft sticks straight out for at least two miles.

Now let us return to the subject of seismic disturbances in the area.

Small wonder!

Perhaps you have stood on a busy city street and felt the subway train rumbling beneath. Or heard the dishes in the dining room rattle as a huge truck hit a pothole in the street.

All sorts of events cause ground rumblings.

But it is assumed that on the Moon volcanic action, with concomitant moonquakes, is responsible for just about every strange event without a ready explanation. (We will see later, for example, that NASA attributes to volcanic action the force causing two "boulders" to dislodge and roll downhill, but the fact that one of the "boulders" rolled up the side of a crater before it rolled downhill is blithely ignored.)

Of course, if enormous motors and gears are not discussed openly with the public, then high seismic readings can be blamed only on volcanic action or moonquakes.

I experimented with small gears and motors. Judging by the effects on delicately balanced objects in the vicinity, I concluded that it is virtually impossible to run things of that nature without some rumbling, or "quakes." The larger the machinery, the larger the disturbances.

What interested me most was the current status of

the seismic recordings. The rumbling activity was happening at present. Dr. Wittcomb, the scientist who had been with NASA during the Moon probes, had told me of the arguments raging in some astrophysical circles.

"You'll get quite a few qualified people now to admit there are strange things on the Moon," he said. "And in unguarded moments some of them even admit their belief in the intelligent origin of the constructions. But the real controversy is over the time problem. Did all that happen eons ago, as some believe? Or is the Moon currently occupied?"

I told,him about my interest in the Bullialdus area, and the seismic recordings. "The quakes could easily be the result of gears grinding, Sam."

"It's possible," Dr. Wittcomb admitted. "But there are other arguments for the 'occupied-now' theory. You know about the gases, the obscurations of some crater floors, the long-lasting flares—"

"And the crater near where Ranger Seven landed!" I cut in. (See Chapter Seven, "Service Station in a Crater?")

"Not to mention proof of actual changes," Dr. Wittcomb continued. "Tell you more about them next time I'm in Washington."

Neither of us ever mentioned UFOs, but they are very real—everyone who has an ounce of sense and who has studied the data knows that—and they have to be based somewhere. The Moon is :a, logical base for all the UFOs skipping around the fringes of our cultures since the dawn of time. Denial by the military and their handmaidens that these UFOs and Moon bases exist can be taken with massive doses of salt; or better yet·—not taken at all. I recall that astronaut Buzz Aldrin pooh-poohed UFOs during a TV interview on the grounds that aliens would logically contact political leaders to set up meetings; but then his status as an Air Force Colonel came back to me, and I reached for the salt.

One fact which gave me pause, however,' and was the biggest argument in favor of the "occupied-eons-ago" theory, was the obvious ruined state of so many objects seen on ..the Moon. The mammoth gear we have been discussing was no exception. It had been blasted by something, something which ripped away part of the outer housing and left the inner teeth exposed, something which had fantastic force.

But we will see later that there is current, purposeful activity on the Moon—and that activity seems to include fixing things up.

The mammoth gear is not the only fantastic object in the Bullialdus-Lubinicky area. There is 'a large structure which appears to be a generator housing.

In plate 3, look straight up above the "gear" and slightly to the left. There you will see a gigantic structure with a slanted roof surface which comes to a rounded top, much like an A-frame which has had its peak rounded off.

Beneath this peak there is something which appears to be a generator. What would be more logical near a mammoth gear than a huge machine by which mechanical energy is changed into electrical energy? In fact, the face under the peak looks much like a direct-current generator, complete with frame and field. The arc of the housing is remarkably perfect. The "struts" to the left of the housing are clean-cut and look precisely as functional struts should.

Below is my interpretation of this "generator":

The generator could run on solar energy or nuclear power or forms of energy we scarcely have inklings of. The generator could make electricity. A lot of electric power would be needed for a below-ground community in the area. Heat is a more valuable commodity on the Moon than on Earth: although the Moon's equatorial areas are very hot in midday, most of the satellite, at any given time, is in the throes of extreme cold. The temperature at the Moon's equator may be over 200 degrees Fahrenheit at noon, but plunges to minus 250 degrees at midnight.

Electricity—for light, for Warmth, to make things go, to move them around, entertain, instruct. The need for electricity is a very logical explanation for the presence of a mammoth generator.

Another logical aspect is the enormous flat roof of the object. In the photo, the roof gleams in the sun. The plane of this roof faces into the sun. Could it be that this flat roof facing into the sun has been designed to take advantage of solar energy?

Water boils at 212 degrees Fahrenheit at sea level on Earth. It will boil at a much lower temperature on the Moon, because of the lower pressure there. We have already seen that the temperature on the Moon at midday exceeds 200 degrees. Water sluiced through capillaries during the middle of the Moon's day would easily get hot enough to power a big generator. As fast as it heats it could go to storage tanks and be replaced by cooler water.

Where would water come from? You will see evidence in the last chapter of this book that the occupants of the Moon regularly siphon water from our own lakes and rivers.

Dr. Sam Wittcomb related to me an entirely different theory about the machinery seen on the Moon. He heard it explained, by an engineer at the Jet Propulsion Lab and by a British physicist at Oxford. The theory is that the Moon is a vast spaceship, that it was driven to our solar system many thousands of years ago after suffering a terrible calamity in space. Its occupants have been engaged in a long, slow effort to repair the damage. Machinery is seen in several places on the Moon. It is nuclear-powered, and will one day be used to drive the Moon out of our orbit into space again.

If this were true, it would not be "our" Moon after all! They would have a right to be there, and we would be the interlopers.

It is refreshing, and not without charm, to run across a full-fledged scientist willing to go further than the so-called state of the art. A Russian, I. S. Shlovskii, did so when he asserted that the two tiny moons of Mars, Phobos and Deimos, have to be artificial because of the way they behave—their speed, direction around Mars, reflectivity, and seeming hollowness. Dr. Allen Hynek, an astronomer, also did it when he broke with some of his fellow scientists and said that UFOs were a serious issue deserving study. Arthur C. Clarke did it when he suggested that the first moon of Jupiter may be a spaceship from outside the solar system.

The most serious objection to the notion of huge gears and generators on the Moon involves levels of technology. You have no doubt already raised this question in your mind. We have on Earth today ways to convert energy to electricity without going through a generator phase. We can shift mechanical force from one axis to another and change speed on the molecular level, setting up gravitational fields, without the need for large gears. An illustrative but oversimplified comparison might be that of the old bulky mechanical calculator and the new hand-held electronic devices.

I agree emphatically with this objection. The terms "gears" and "generators" have been used as convenient handles to label what are clearly intelligent contrivances. I do not know what, precisely, these intelligent contrivances are. They might be gears and generators pretty much as we know them, constructed eons ago by space races earlier in their development period, 'although this is hard to believe.

Or they might be successor devices, depending on technological advances far beyond us. Remember that the best bet is that any intelligent extraterrestrials we come across will have a technology that is beyond our comprehension.

The points on which Dr. Wittcomb and I agree are that"' they are manufactured, capable of controlled rotation, seem to have been damaged, and were built by extraterrestrials.,.

In the next chapter we will see other kinds of machinery engaged in "pushing the Moon around": moving ground, sculpting, etc. Keep in mind that the technological advances which reduce the need for some functions do not reduce the need, necessarily, for size. For example, if you want to take a ten-foot scoop of dirt out of an embankment, you might have the most sophisticated equipment and power source possible, but the need will still exist for something large enough for that ten-foot scoop.

One closing thought: although there is evidence of considerable activity on the surface of the Moon, the inhabitants have not—judging by all the thousands of close-up pictures available—littered the ground. But They may be denuding the Moon of its mineral resources. And They may be interested in what resources we have left on Earth.

David Freeman, energy consultant, says that our natural gas resources are almost gone and that oil resources will dry up within forty years. "We might see a lot of war on this planet as it becomes very difficult for everyone to share what little we have."

Fred Ikle, Director of the U.S. Arms Control and Disarmament Agency, says: "The world will be a very different place on the morning after a nuclear explosion. . . . Ten to fifteen years down the road, it could happen. . . . The lack,, of solutions does keep me awake at night."

In the year 2000, the world population will be six billion. In 2033 it will be twelve billion. In 2100 it will be forty-eight billion. Dr. James Echols, associated with the Population Reference Bureau, says that unless a way is found to reduce this horde of people, a combination of food shortages, disease, wars, pollution, and social chaos will combine to kill us off. He says we are too late.

The chairman of a National Academy of Sciences committee on water-quality policy, Professor Gordon Wollman, says, "We're on a collision course with the future."

Studies with rats have shown that dramatic increases of their population in a limited area cause their behavior to become erratic, and many of them die.

Are They biding their time on the Moon, waiting to take over after our ultimate catastrophes?

And surely you read Charles Berlitz's The Bermuda Triangle (Doubleday, 1974), in which he quotes the last words of the pilot of a plane lost in that strange area: "Don't come after me . . . They look like they are from outer space."

CHAPTER FOUR
Pushing the Moon Around: Super Rigs

In the first chapter we discussed the importance of forgetting old ways of thinking.

When we think of ground-movers, what springs to mind? A big bulldozer with wheels six feet in diameter and a blade in front which can push several tons of dirt at once? A steam shovel with teeth as long as your arm which can bite into a hillside and fill a truck with one scoop?

Forget it. There are rigs on the Moon several miles long, capable of demolishing the rim of a seventy-five-mile-wide crater in the same time it takes us to level ten acres.

What Does an Octagon Mean?

On August 26, 1966, NASA's Lunar Orbiter I spacecraft took a picture of a crater on the hidden side of the Moon. The picture is a treasure trove for geologists, astrophysicists, selenologists, and people whose minds are not in a straitjacket. It shows a thirty-one-mile-wide crater which has impinged on the walls of a smaller crater.

Both craters are clearly distinguishable as octagons (See plate 4, 66-H-1293).

One is conditioned to think of natural geometrical

shapes in terms of snowflakes and crystals. (Beehives and their ilk are, after all, the result of intelligent activity.)

Is this one example of the need to do away with old thinking? Is there a natural way in which an octagon can be formed on the Moon—an octagon thirty-one miles in diameter?

The Larousse Encyclopedia of Astronomy states: "*...Many craters are quite clearly polygonal in shape. This no doubt results from the intersection of the cracks which gave them birth.*" Other works on the Moon ignore the fascinating shapes of craters completely, or flatly admit it to be a problem. There seems to be agreement that these kinds of craters could not result from impact.

Larousse's statement refers to the possibility that magma from beneath the outer layer of the Moon erupted to form crater walls, and then the crater collapsed of its own weight. But the walls of the crater in plate 4 are not raised. They are clean-cut, level with the .ground.

Moreover, there are marvelous examples of constructions inside the crater. But before we touch upon these constructions, it may be productive to consider the differences between the near and far sides of the Moon.

Not Just "More of the Same"

A look at both sides of the Moon reveals striking differences. In addition to having fewer seas—the dark, flat, smooth maria—the other side of the Moon is more heavily cratered. and the craters are clustered together.

Many of these craters are polygonal, or have overtones of various geometric shapes.

Why would one side of the Moon have lots more craters —craters with interesting shapes—than the other? The eruption of magma along crack lines with a later collapsing of the center is a believable theory to account for polygonal shapes. But study of the near side of the Moon reveals countless numbers of craters which are perfectly round, and study of the far side reveals many more which are not.

Some craters are octagons; some are hexagons; a few are squares. While there are a few crater chains visible on the Moon—mostly on the near side—the preponderance of craters appears to be randomly located.

What are we to make of a hexagon within a square? Two hexagons not merely having a common wall, but intruding on each other? I have sketched some of these more interesting shapes below:

If They are working the Moon—and all the evidence points in that direction—then there is a good reason for the hidden side of the Moon being so different: it has been worked more.

The above shapes make it difficult for me to believe that these, craters were made from extruding magma. Small wonder that there is still controversy over crater origins!

"Super Rig"

At the base of the rim in the larger crater (plate 4), at half-past two o'clock, is_an object which is too wispy to show up well when reproduced in this book. The wispiness is probably due to its structure; an object of this size would retain all of its strength at a very low weight if it were filigreed. This is the basic building principle of triangles, and is illustrated in television towers and boom cranes, which are built of struts and crosspieces rather than being solid. Notice, when you have a chance, the shadow cast by these cranes and towers. "Insubstantial" and "wispy" would be good adjectives to use.

The object pivots at the junction—just where you would expect it to pivot. Its two main struts rising from the ground (the wispy elements) are very straight and parallel. There appears to be a filament of some sort which raises and lowers the horizontal piece leading to the scoop. There is a long thin device which runs from the base of the object down the hill toward the center of the crater, ending in an oblong plate which (as we shall see in later chapters) is found elsewhere on the Moon and is perhaps a connection to a power source.

Below is how this object in the crater appears:

Equipment that size—several miles long, with moving parts—is well within our own technology on Earth. We build subways, jetliners, ships which are floating cities. We build dams which stretch for miles. But our needs have not been sufficient to warrant the construction of ground-moving equipment more than several yards long.

Consider the Moon and its occupants, and Their possible aims. If They are mining the craters and there are no communities nearby, huge equipment would make sense. They could be looking for an element which is widely dispersed through the Moon's crust but which is extensively mixed with other elements. Nickel and aluminum spring to mind, or gaseous elements such as oxygen and hydrogen. In this case. They would sift or smelt or (out of that straitjacket again) scientifically treat very large quantities at a time. Or could They be digging out from a calamity which struck Them a long time ago?

Whatever Their aims, the object is there, the crater is being pushed around and further sculpted, and much of the area smacks of activity and construction.

Fleur-de-lis?

Inside the crater rim at ten o'clock is a marvelous sculpturing highlighted by the sun. It is a perfect design, at the top of a rock pillar, symmetrical from top to bottom. Another design is next to it. My version of both are below. The fleur-de-lis is particularly interesting because it appears on the floor of another crater being Worked (plate 5 [72-H-1109]).

Increasingly in this book we will see evidence of a marked flair for symbolic and expressive art on a big scale. The astronauts marvelled at these sights, judging by their expressions and use of code words for them as they circled close to the Moon's surface. Entire mountains seem to be carved out into shapes appealing to their aesthetic nature. This is particularly true along great valleys and in the highlands. Was this one of the culture traits Jacques Vallee was referring to when he said he and his associates believed the contours of an amazingly complex extraterrestrial civilization were becoming apparent?

Super Rig 1971

A most remarkable photo was taken by the astronauts during the Apollo 14 flights around the Moon. It is the clearest picture of a mechanical rig on the Moon coming to my attention. I have po doubt that

Alan Shepard, Stuart Roosa and Edgar Mitchell saw it first visually from the space ship and then took the picture.

We know from the tapes how the astronauts reacted to other phenomena. Discovery of this huge object might have gone like this:

ROOSA: "Hey! There's Annbell! [Or Barbara?] Just like the one we saw during that pass yesterday!"

SHEPARD: "Check. Houston won't believe this. Look at the tracks running into the crater, right up to the ledge—"

MITCHELL: "She's sitting right on the ledge! It must be over a mile high! And did you see that? The light flare coming from the dark part of the crater rim? It's just below Annbell."

ROOSA: "How could anyone miss it? Cameras, don't fail us now!"

The result is 71-H-781 (plate 6), taken five years after the picture of the other super rig discussed above.

The similarities between the two rigs are striking. And similarities, as you know, are at the core of science. Symptoms of physical ailments are grouped so diseases can be named and similar medicines prescribed. Similar biological species are grouped for identification and naming. New scientific findings are judged on the basis of the similarity of results achieved by other scientists using the same methods. One sighting of the rare Siberian smew on our East coast might be a fluke, but similar sightings by more than one person take on the cloak of scientific truth. It i3 no accident that the two mechanical goliaths look alike.

Super rig 1971 is on a terraced, inside rim of an

unnamed crater on the far side of the Moon. It stands up straight. It is constructed of filigreed metal (triangles and space) for strength and lightness, thus casting no observable shadow. A "cord" runs from its base down the side of the crater. All of these properties are similar to those of super rig 1966.

My sketch of super rig 1971 follows. Note that on the right of the same flat terrace two other rigs are working. They also are constructed of filigreed metal. They stand up straight and have two pieces working from a fulcrum.

Cords run from their bases. The result of their efforts is clearly seen. They have made an even cut straight down into the terrace. The cut (notch) is straight as a die. Something straight stretches across the gap. They will continue this work until the cut reaches all the way to the crater floor, at which point the entire chunk of ground will be sent crashing down. Other machines will then take over the work of sifting, talking away, smelting, or whatever procedures they are carrying out.

The size of the crater is not given by NASA. There is absolutely no information given on the back of this photo beyond the words, "From lunar orbit, the Apollo 14 crew photographed these Moon scenes." Taken by itself, there are no guidelines in the photo for judging size. But we may guess in this case by assuming that the 1971 rig is of the same order of size as the 1966 rig. In this event we arrive at the rough estimate of one and one-half miles for the rig, and at least three miles high for the chunk of ground from crater floor to where the rigs are perched.

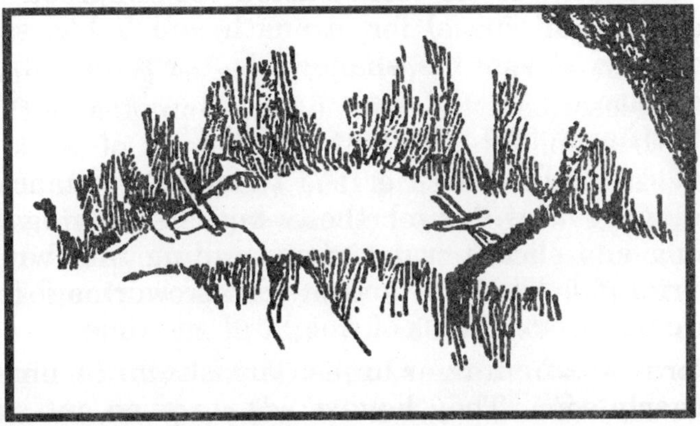

Do you think these huge contrivances are built on some home planet or on the Moon? If the latter: imagine the extent of the manufacturing going on there! But no matter where they are built, vast service-repair functions are no doubt needed. The other phenomena you will read about in this book (gas jets, clouds, mists, lights, movement, etc.) become even more logical and understandable, in the light of our knowledge of these mechanical wonders.

"X" Stands for "X-drone"

The most numerous kind of "rig" on the Moon is a huge object looking like two crossed earthworms. They vary in size from under a mile to three miles in any direction. They are not straight-edged and dull metallic in appearance as are the "super rigs" discussed above. Although they can lift one or two legs in doing their work, they do not, as do "super rigs," stand erect. They lie flat on the ground. Their function, as we shall see, differs from the digging and ground-moving functions of "super rig." In later chapters we will see how these X-drones can change functions, even change an entire leg. For now we are interested in them as pulverizers of rock.

I call these rigs "X-drones." It is as good a name as any; it describes their shape and connotes work. And work they do! Whenever there is a lot of work to be done in certain parts of the Moon, the chances are excellent you will find these big X's slaving away; ripping and slicing crater rims, pulling taut whatever material it is They use to stretch across ribs for cover, lifting hundreds of tons of weight at one time.

Some outstanding examples are shown in photo 69-H-25 (plate 7). The clearest ones are on the rim at twelve o'clock, on the rim at one o'clock and at the bottom of the crater.

Look carefully at the photo. You will see that the rim I from twelve to three o'clock has evenly spaced slices cut I into it. They are all ready to be pulled out and sent crashing to the crater floor. The X-drones will have a role in pulling out the slices and pulverizing them. Perhaps they also did the slicing. Clearly, gravity and power pose no problems for these huge devices!

The rubble in the lower right-hand quadrant seems to have been cleared. away, while the rubble on the entire left side remains. What has happened to the rubble? It does not appear to have been cast on the ground outside the crater —it would have obliterated the tiny craterlets which are visible, and the ground would look different. It seems evident that the rubble is lugged away and used for something. Mining or construction are possibilities.

There are other X-drones in the picture. Most of them have a leg raised enough so that it casts a shadow. One has two legs raised. The contortions these machines go through in their work is most interesting. I have seen the following positions:

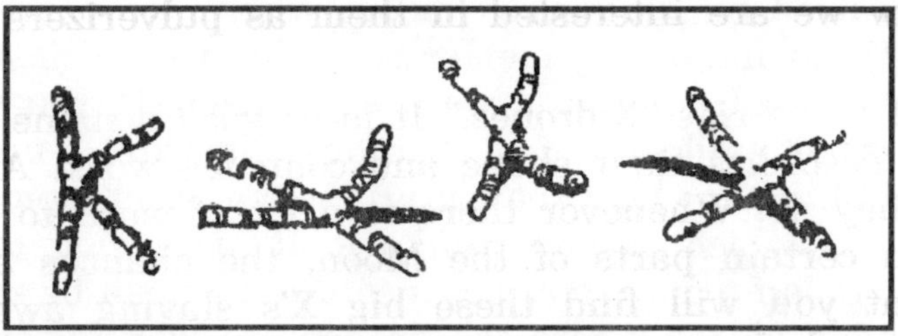

The Incomplete Circle

Did you notice something else interesting about this crater? It is an astounding feature! The circle of the crater rim has two ends which do not meet.

I have performed many experiments with sand and powder, trying to learn what kinds of patterns result from what kinds of impactions. Theoretically and practically, it is impossible to create, by either impaction or volcanic action, this, kind of configuration. This leaves the "exudation of magma and collapse of the interior" theory to account for the crater shape. I do not believe this is tenable. When X-drones are seen working on the rim, when slices cut are equal to the distance between the discrepant rim lines, the obvious answer is that the shape of the crater is determined by the Moon's occupants.

X-Drones Raise Dust

Another outstanding example of X-drones at work in craters is shown in plate 8, 72-H-837.

Arrows are drawn to the principal ones. Note the drone with an arm raised high, casting a shadow. Note also that dust is raised above the place where one of them is working. There are many examples of dust raised where the drones are working. How does dust get raised on an airless moon, where wind does not exist? An impacting meteorite could stir up dust in a small area (if the area were large enough, you would see other evidence of a striking meteorite) , but you would have to shoot the picture at the exact moment of impact, which seems unlikely. It does not take a statistician to say that, because the dust can be seen in so many places where the drones are working, the X-drones must be "kicking up a storm."

The Sample Scoop

Look back at the "incomplete circle" crater—especially at the craterlet in the rim at three o'clock. It is most unnatural. It has all the earmarks of a sample scoop; that is, they took a mammoth scoop to see what was there. The "sample scoop" is rampant on the Moon in close-up shots, and is a plausible explanation for many of the small anomalous craters.

It would be interesting to see later shots of these craters. But I have searched in vain. My inquiries have resulted in no leads. Certainly, a later shot would show a different pattern—more of the rim would be gone, more rubble taken away, and perhaps the X-drones would have moved on to other craters, other rims.

Taking Away a Central Mountain

There is an area east of Mare Smythii, on the other side of the Moon near the crater Saenger, which contains an entire story of the work being done by mechanical rigs (plate 5, [72-H-1109]).

First, a sketch of the crater in question.

There are some interesting points to be made about this very active crater. The rig working just left of center is not an X-drone. It is a new kind of rig. It is straight and rigid along its entire length. For convenience, we will label it "T- scoop." The T-scoop has removed an enormous area of the crater's central peak, and is at the edge, still slaving. Nearby are piles of rubble, perhaps placed there by the T-scoop. Another T-scoop is on the rim of the crater at nine o'clock.

Near the mechanical rig is a configuration on the ground resembling the fleur-de-lis seen in the other crater where a large rig was working. The fleur-de-lis may be the symbol of this particular group or its particular function. (Later will see that X-drones, when they perform a certain function in small craters, have their own unique symbol.)

Most remarkable, the crater has two ends of the circle which do not meet, similar to another crater seen earlier in this chapter. The rim is being systematically knocked down by something which goes around in a spiral.

Rigs Which Spew Out Filaments

There is yet another kind of rig on the Moon whose function beggars explanation. One beautiful example is a Matsui (Kwasan Observatory, Japan) picture reproduced in Patrick Moore's book^ Survey of the Moon. You can check it by "getting a copy of his book and turning to plate 8.

The rig show's up in a remarkable photo of Pythagoras and the Sinus Iridum. Until the NASA pictures, I think this Japanese observatory produced the finest lunar pictures. ("Pythagoras," incidentally, is a most fitting name for this crater, in view of the many geometric formations in the vicinity.)

Turn the photo sideways so the horizon is at the top. Below is my version of the area. The crater in question is reproduced in a larger scale beside it.

Notice the object on the upper side of the squared crater. It seems to be spewing some sort of filament across the expanse of the crater. Or is it merely connected to the objects on the opposite rim?

Usually, when these objects are sighted, there is another object of a similar nature facing the first one, ready to do whatever it does with the other end of the filament. There are several good examples of this kind of rig on the Moon; later, we shall see one in the King Crater area. The objects are shaped like long bowling pins or enormous cannons. They are one to two miles in length, and are found pointing their smaller ends or noses upward, doing whatever job they are called upon to do.

But who knows? Could it be that they are playing,

not working?

Flying Machines or Mammoth Yurts?

A discussion of large objects which appear to be doing something, or serving a function, should perhaps include

the gleaming white hemispheres which abound, particularly on the floor of Tycho.

These are not the phenomena referred to by astronomers as domes. The classic domes may, as NASA points out elsewhere, be the result of upward movement of magma which has warped the overlying rock. These classic domes are irregular mounds. They tend to be flattish rather than perfect hemispheres, and often have a craterlet at the peak.

The hemispheres under discussion never vary. They are symmetrical, have a slight scalloping on the straight edge, and are on the same order of size: an eighth of a mile to three-quarters of a mile in diameter, averaging about four hundred yards.

I have found no area where they differ radically in size. Within a single area they tend to be similar. In Tycho they are about four hundred yards in diameter. Twenty or thirty of them are clustered in a neighborhood of the Tycho floor (plate 9, 169-H1206]).

Typically, they look like the following sketches. The object on the right is found at the base of one of the hemispheres. It is smaller, perhaps two hundred yards in diameter, and flatter than the larger domes. An object identical to this was photographed by Ralph Nicholson while taking a picture of Sputnik-2 in 1957. (Reported by science writer Otto Binder in What We Really Know About Flying Saucers [Fawcett Gold Medal, 1967], p. 158.)

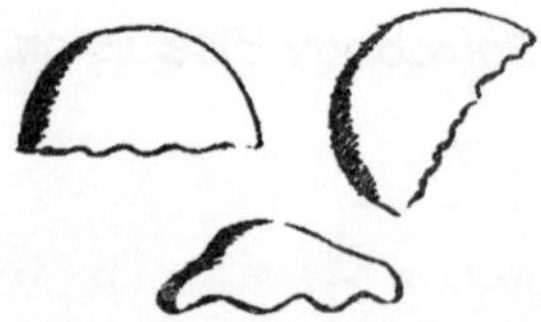

Some Mongol nomads make a circular domed tent by stretching skins over a latticework frame. It is called a yurt. A yurt a quarter of a mile in diameter and lacquered pure white would look like a hemisphere in Tycho.

The temptation is to call this a dwelling place. How neat! We have seen evidence of the Moon occupants at work, and now we see Their abodes! But I tend to think most of Them live underground, and that small domes of perfect architecture, are probably tied in with locomotion or work. (The exception to this may be the large domes on platforms which we shall see in Chapter Sixteen, "Assorted Oddities.")

There is, however, no evidence for saying with assurance, more than this: they are certainly artificial; they may be used for living, moving about, working, or yet some other purpose; they are different from that natural phenomenon astronomers refer to as domes; and they are fairly uniform in size and shape.

There are other rigs on the Moon, many considerably smaller. Evidence for their existence will be seen in Chapter Eight, "Things That Move Around." We see their tracks. We see their lights. We see the dust that they raise. Either the science, of astronomy is in its darkest period— and God knows there have been dark periods!—or the distance between its practitioners and the people has become astronomical.

And perhaps you missed the report by the late Dr. I van Sanderson, Argosy's science editor, in August 1970: "Many phenomena observed on the lunar surface appear to have been devised by intelligent beings. Now, U.S. and Russian Moon probes have photographed two such 'constructions' at close range."

CHAPTER FIVE
Spraying Out the Craters

There are three pictures taken by the Apollo 16 spacecraft which reveal the technological glory of the Moon occupants, and clarify their work habits as well.

The pictures are plates 10, Hand 12—No. 72-H-834, . 72-H-836, and 72-H-839. The 834 and 839 photos were taken about fifty revolutions, or two days, apart. When looked at from the point of view of discrepancies between what is happening in one and not the other, a fascinating story is told.

The area is in between King Crater's southern rim and a large unnamed crater with a "ponding effect" bottom. *

The evidence of change was found as a result of Dr. Wittcomb's challenge to me. I began to compile a list of all NASA photos showing a given area of the Moon at different times, from different aspects. The discovery that more than one shot of Tycho existed spurred me on. Soon the collection was impressive—three of the Alpine Valley, at least two of the Hyginus Rille, several of Copernicus. I haunted the photo tubs at NASA..

King Crater and its environs made my hundreds of hours of work worthwhile. First I checked the 836 photo, around the edges of the big unnamed crater and the

* "Ponding effect" is a flat relatively low area with an homogeneous appearance, such as would result from water trapped in a depression;dried mud leveled by water once there; or sand sprayed evenly over an area.

highlands in back of it. In the highlands was a small crater and something was coming up out of it, arching to the right in a high stream which came down far outside the rim. Of all the sprays I was to find later, this would prove to be the largest and most impressive.

I found another spray in the 834 photo, this time in front of the big unnamed crater. Whatever the spray was, it could not last forever. It had a beginning and an end. The big question which made my hands tremble as I picked up photo 839 was: Would the spray end in one of the other pictures of the area?

But the other good photo of the area, 839, had been taken about two days earlier, not later. In that picture the crater did not show a spray. The evidence of change was backwards from what I expected: instead of a spray beginning and then stopping, I had proof that it was quiescent, nonexistent, in the earlier picture (839) and active in the later picture (834).

My excitement was so great at this point that it was hard to sit down and work instead of picking up the telephone. But the work was more important than telling people.

A careful examination of the earlier picture with the quiescent spray revealed fantastic detail inside the crater, and immediately outside, on the rim. The kind of a rig we met in Chapter Four, the mechanical monster I call an X-drone, was working on the inside slope. It was working in exactly the same spot from which the spray would emanate in the 834 picture taken two days later.

Considerable deductive reasoning power is not needed to arrive at the following conclusions: X-drones have something to do with the spraying process; and either craters are sprayed out totally (the evidence to date is that it takes place primarily in funnel-shaped craters), or existing craters are enlarged or changed.

The spraying operation may have something to do with the search for raw materials, although one can think of other reasons for spraying out craters. The search for structural defects in the Moon's crust, the need for craters of a certain shape and size for landing berths, archaeology, recreation or competition, are all prospects. But who knows how an extraterrestrial thinks? You can perhaps conceive of other possible reasons for the sprays—and both of us may be wrong!

Before we discuss further what is in these craters, it is important to consider the crosses that are found outside the rims.

What Do the Crosses Mean?

Outside almost every crater being sprayed out, a gleaming cross can be seen abutting the rim. Possibly every spraying crater has a cross, but a few elude us because of picture angle, etc. The crosses are perfect, are not shaped like Latin or Celtic crosses but intersect in the exact middle, and most of the time they are tipped with one end on the ground and the opposite end raised up so that they cast a shadow. In a full color photo enlarged by NASA, the cross on the edge of one crater shows up as bright blue.

Below are sketches of the spraying crater discussed above:

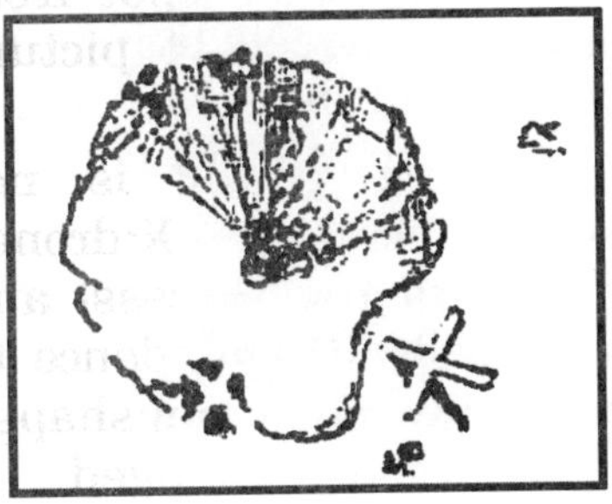

There are other kinds of crosses on the Moon. It abounds with them. But when the cross is used in situations other than in conjunction with the spraying process, it invariably is of a different shape.

For example, there is a beautiful shot of Kepler, at an oblique angle, and toward the camera a few miles from the crater lip is a Latin cross four miles long and raised off of the ground half a mile. It is in a rectangle. The Latin (or Roman) cross near Keplar looks like this (plate 13, [67-H-201]):

It is not, of course, our Roman cross. The simple nature of the cross as a symbol would make it in demand throughout the galaxy. But it is important to differentiate this from the gleaming crosses on the edges of craters being sprayed out. They are not the same.

Not long ago I was on a jet coming into National Airport from Chicago. The man beside me had slept the whole trip, and now he awoke and began to talk. He was on his way to supervise construction projects for Arab countries in North Africa. He'd been living with language records for four months, and the strain of that and sweating out the contract showed in his face.

"Suppose you had to build something at intervals of fifty miles across the desert," I said. We were buckling our seat belts. "What are the main problems?"

He began ticking them off. The third problem was the one I was waiting for.

"We'd have to put signals on top of the buildings," he said. "Signals which could be seen a long distance from the air. Ever flown over the desert?"

"Only at night."

He shook his head. "Without identification marks you're stuck. And if the functions of the various stations or buildings are different, you'd better have some signals that tell what the functions are, too."

So there are craters on the Moon of a certain size—my sample so far indicated a range of one to four miles in diameter—with X-drones working in them, spraying out the sand and breccia. They have signals on the rim large enough to be seen from a long distance above the ground, perhaps a hundred miles or more. The signal is a cross of

absolutely perfect dimensions, gleaming' white, and tilted so it casts a shadow and cannot blend in with the ground.

Or (what may be more important) perhaps it is tilted so that the dirt sprayed outside the crater cannot bury it.

This thesis had to be further tested. I began the search for other craters in which X-drones might be working. I did not have to look far. In the previously examined photo, plate 12, showing a vast upland area to the west of King Crater and the unnamed smooth-floored crater, there was a total of five examples which supported the thesis. It is apparent from the data that X-drones flail at ridges to pulverize rock. They can also spray sand and dirt out of craters. The craters in which X-drones perform this function always range from one to four miles in diameter. Wherever an X-drone is working and spraying in such craters, a large gleaming white cross rests on the rim; a cross which says to sky observers and travelers: "There is an X-drone spraying here."

Three other conical or funnel-shaped craters—all located in plate 12—were being worked on by X-drones.

Only a few scant miles away from the original crater discovered with a spray (out on the pond-effect flat bottom of the unnamed crater) is another funnel-shaped hole containing an X-drone and a signal cross.

It contains one other interesting feature: a trail leading from outside the crater to the X-drone. This indicates that either the X-drone was dragged, or made its own trail, into the crater; or a pipeline, electrical conduit, or other energy- supplying hose leads from a source to the rig.

This crater is depicted on page 67.

Toward the bottom of the photo, near the top of the ridge, is another funnel-shaped crater which has both the signal cross outside the lip and the mechanical rig inside. Allowing for distance—it is much nearer to the camera— this crater is smaller than the other. It is possible, of course, that there is more work to be done in this crater and the drone will ultimately make it larger. It looks like this (the following drawing):

The next example of X-drone activity in a funnel-shaped crater is nearer still to the camera, on the other side of the ridge. The pattern changes here, becoming more interesting and mysterious. There is a large area on the near outer lip which has been scraped clean, ready for a signal cross. (Wherever there is a signal cross, the ground is always smoothed out.) An imperfect cross is found there, or the marking where one had been. The sun glare inside the crater where

the X-drone is is too great to see ail parts of the rig. But one leg can be seen, raised up, catching the sun's rays. A spray can be seen coming from this raised leg. In the direction of the spray, outside the crater, is what appears to be a smaller X-drone. The crater and environs look like this:

There are other suggestive craters in the same photo, but none are as clear-cut as these. There are magnificent sprays coming out of craters in several other pictures.

All of the spray activity I have documented is on the other side of the Moon. But interesting activity of different kinds is found on the near side, in Tycho, the Alpine Valley, Mare Crisium, Plato, and so on. What are we to conclude? What does the activity suggest?

First, it is remarkable that so much similar phenomena is seen in a single area. Close examination of the Bullialdus-Lubinicky area or Tycho reveals not a single example of the X-drone, a funnel-shaped crater being worked, or a signal cross on the crater lip. From this we can draw either of two viable conclusions: the function or purpose of the Moon occupants in this King

Crater area is so unique that X-drones are needed there but not in other parts of the Moon; or there are entirely different space races on the Moon—with Their own geographical areas, technology, needs, cultures.

Second, funnel-shaped craters would be efficient and sensible probes for determining the underground ore, rock,

and gas content. The shape would minimize risk of landslides, cave-ins of the crater sides. The constant shape would indicate that test diggings had already been made there and imply "Don't waste your time."

Third, the obvious conclusion is that many of the craters of . a certain size and .shape we see on the Moon have not been created by meteoric impact or volcanism or any other natural cause, but by purposeful intelligent activity on the part of the occupants. This gives rise to the question: How many other kinds of craters on the Moon have also been artificially made?

Fourth, some smooth ponding-effect ground is not a relic of the distant past when the surface of the Moon was molten, or of lava flow, but is the result of spraying by X- drones. There are many examples of this. Another related phenomenon which creates smooth areas is falling sand and dust on the sides of ridges, where X-drones are working. The best example of this can be seen on the inside rim of Kings Crater, plate 8. Where X-drones are raising dust, ledges below appear smooth from a layer of fallen dust. There are many such smooth areas on terraces and shelves.

I took these pages to a physicist friend at the Bureau of Standards, with the plea that he read them critically. He used a blue pencil here and there, then looked back over the sketches of the craters being sprayed and stared at me for half a minute without speaking. Small furrows were around his eyes. He tried to smile, but it did not come off.

"You're kidding."

I shook my head. "Straight stuff."

"I read the Bulletin of Atomic Scientists, Science, and

God knows how many other periodicals. Not in a single one of them ..."

"Maybe you don't read the right things," I said. "Maybe you don't take the trouble to look at the Apollo and Orbiter photos. Maybe you don't talk to the right people."

I was thinking of Dr. Sam Wittcomb and my amateur astronomer friend, Bill Vaughan, and Joseph Goodavage, who had listened to a lot of the Apollo tapes and heard some startling things, and a small number of scientists around the country who'd opened up a little in talking with me.

The physicist was still shaking his head. "They devoted most of an issue of the Bulletin to the Moon a while back.

All about the chemistry and physics and geology of the Moon."

"November '73 issue," I said. "It was a good one."

His eyes glazed',"' and as I thanked him and we shook hands, he didn't really see me. He was perhaps wondering if maybe his peers in physics who'd been close to the Moon probes and all those scientists who'd been through the same mill he'd gone through didn't know something they hadn't communicated to him. I wanted to say something like "But you didn't have a need to know, old buddy," but my irony would have been lost, and I'm glad it didn't come out. Who did have a need to know? Nine men in the Pentagon? Or anybody who pays taxes? I wanted to cry then for Renaissance Man-Woman, who—if not already dead—was surer than hell getting killed off fast by the security monster.

I mailed a copy of this chapter to Sam Wittcomb. A reply arrived two weeks later. His letter read as follows:

It's a piece of the puzzle, a damned important piece, but that's all. You're starting to behave like a professional. To you that may not be a compliment. I would not have written it that way, but I suppose you have to make concessions in a popular book.

As for your speculations on what they're doing—you can start with the search for raw materials. My opinion is, though, that this is a side occupation to meet their needs on the Moon—not to lug back home. Which leaves their basic purpose still up in the air.

God knows how much worthwhile ore will be left when we finally take over, if we ever do. It's a problem for our progeny. Do you think they'll go away just because we tell' them to? Is there such a thing as territorial rights 250,000 miles out from a planet, as a country on Earth has jurisdictional rights for so many miles out to sea? Or should a planet have an automatic right to all its moons? I can see opportunities for interplanetary lawyers.

This line of chat assumes, of course, that they took over our Moon and didn't drive their own moon here from someplace else!

Keep up the hard work. Did you know that someone in the Pentagon has speculated that the Moon's occupants may have a purpose for humans up there? Maybe old Charlie Fort had more prescience than we give him credit for. Speaking of Washington, you may be interested in the enclosed poem by David McCord I found somewhere.

The poem follows. I did not sleep much the night after getting Sam's letter.

Go Fly a Saucer

I've seen one flying saucer. Only when
It flew across our sight in 1910
We little thought about the little men.
But let's suppose the little men were there
to cozy such a disc through foreign air:
Connecticut was dark, but didn't scare.
I wonder what they thought of us, and why

They chose the lesser part of Hailey's sky,
And went away and let the years go by
Without return? Or did they not get back
To Mars or Venus through the cosmic flak?
At least they vanished, every spaceman Jack.
Now they are with us in the books, in air,
In argument, in hope, in fear, in spare
Reports from men aloft who saw them there.
The day one saucer cracks, the greatest egg
Since dinosaur and dodo shook a leg
Will give new meaning to the prefix meg.
Some say the saucers with their little race
Of little men from Littlesphere in space
Have sensed our international disgrace.
And when the thing blows over, up, or what,
They'll gladly land and give us all they've got
So Earth shall cease to be a trouble spot.
One fact as old as Chaucer, Saucer Men:
You may be little as a bantam hen,
But Earth has specialized in little men.

—DAVID MCCORD, Imagination's Other Place: Poems of Science and Mathematics, Compiled by Helen Plotz (Little, Brown and Company, 1955)

And the statement by Charles Fort Sam referred to is in his New Lands (Holt, Rinehart and Winston, Inc., 1941; Ace paperback): "One supposes that if extra-mundane vessels have sometimes come close to this earth, then sailing away, terrestrial aeronauts may have occasionally left this earth, or may have been seised and carried away from this earth" and "So then the little nearby moon—and it is populated by Lilliputians."

CHAPTER SIX
Change on the Moon: Knocking Down the Ridges

The NASA scientist and I walked from the Space Science Data Center at Goddard to the library. He was going to introduce me to the system in which a few key words fed into a computer retrieved an entire bibliography. I wanted to learn more about mascons, those big masses of something beneath the dark maria of the Moon. The masses which disconcerted the scientists and caused gravitational anomalies. He wanted to talk about King Crater.

"Others have struggled with King Crater," he remarked as we waited for the lunchtime traffic to stream toward the main gate. "It raises more questions than it answers."

"The area is loaded with these mechanical rigs I call 'X-drones,' " I said. I was trying to shock. "Almost two miles long."

His face was impassive.

"It's where so many craters are being sprayed out," I said.

The word "sprayed" did it. He turned in surprise.

"So you've noticed the sprays. Some conjecture that they aren't sprays, but *solids.*

"It's occupied me day and night for weeks," I admitted.

"*It's been discussed around NASA.*"

It was my turn to be surprised. I had not expected one of the NASA scientists to admit this—although an administrative official at NASA had told me of the attention that the sprays were getting. But when I pursued the subject he showed reticence and would not go further. We dropped the subject of spraying out the craters.

"King Crater, deserves a lot of study,", he said as we entered the library. "There are quite" "a few different shots

of it, as you must know. Different days . . . different lighting'. . . different aspects."

I remembered this conversation when I went next to the audio-visual shop at NASA to browse in the photo tubs.

One of the problems in looking for particular pictures in the tubs is that the brief description you see is not always helpful or complete. It might say "Uplands region, other side of the Moon, Apollo 16 flight" and leave you hanging as to which crater or mountain range is represented. The backs of the photos, which usually have a more complete description, are hidden; the photos are back-to-back in celluloid enclosures. The only way to handle the problem was to get as many photos as possible which were missing from my collection and then examine them at my leisure.

I spent the better part of a day there, and the time was worth it. In the grab bag were two shots I had not previously recognized as being of the King Crater area. One was a bird's-eye view, a very long-distance shot, which I sent to a photographer's shop in downtown Washington to have blown up. It came back on a Friday, and the next morning I set all the associated photos out on a table and went to work. Saturday night I was still at the table, under a strong light, and when I went to bed at three thirty it was to lie with my eyes staring starkly at the ceiling, still seeing in my mind the fantastic sights scattered in that one area near King Crater.'

We return to plates 10, 11 and 12. There is a long ridge separating King Crater from the 100-kilometer crater with the smooth "pond" in it. The ridge forms the interior wall of King Crater and the long sloping rim of the other. At the base of the ridge nearest the camera are some old friends as well as some new oddities. What entranced me was that now the oddities began to jibe together, to click, and sense began to emerge out of the struggle to find and understand Their purpose.

Gouging Out a Mountain

With equipment ranging up to forty times bigger than anything used on Earth, the occupants of the Moon have set about pulverizing a mountain. The mountain is 3.6 miles high. There is nothing comparable to this undertaking on Earth. It is as though we tried to break up a large chunk of the Himalayas, and not in one indiscriminate swoop, with nuclear-energy blasts, but far more delicately so that a concurrent purpose such as mining could be served.

Plate 12, taken more from an overhead position and closer to the ridge than the other photos, shows that huge scoops have been taken out of the ridge and sent crashing to the ground as rubble.

I think it possible that these industrious workers on the Moon use advanced techniques for slicing and cutting into mountains and crater rims. One example might be laser beams. Another could be small controlled explosions. Obscuring dust clouds have been seen on the Moon for two hundred years. The only way they can occur on a windless surface is for dust to be forced artificially into action—by insulting the surface of the Moon in some way. Explosions or large-scale flailing might well constitute that insult.

Regardless of the method used to soften up the breccia or slice into the mountain ridge, the end-result activity seems to involve use of X-drones. They perform, as we shall see, more than one function.

X-drones with Different Attachments

Americans have the reputation for being the best engineers, although the Germans and Japanese are right up there too. Not scientists: engineers. It may surprise you to learn that the . bulk of great scientific leaps ahead in the world can be attributed to people from other countries (e.g., Europe and China) or to people who cut their eye teeth in foreign schools. If you doubt this, make a list of the biggest scientific breakthroughs you can name, and then consider who was responsible. I think this is due to the American science-training plant's turning out people too strongly oriented toward success as opposed to intellectual curiosity—too quick to take cheap shots at one another and at those who "invade" their domain.

So here we are with this great reputation for engineering, but the occupants of the Moon can run rings around us in terms of engineering feats.

For a case in point, look at the foot of the ridge in plate 12. There is a large X-drone there, one of the largest I have seen on the Moon. It measures at least a mile and a half and probably more from tip to tip. It looks like this:

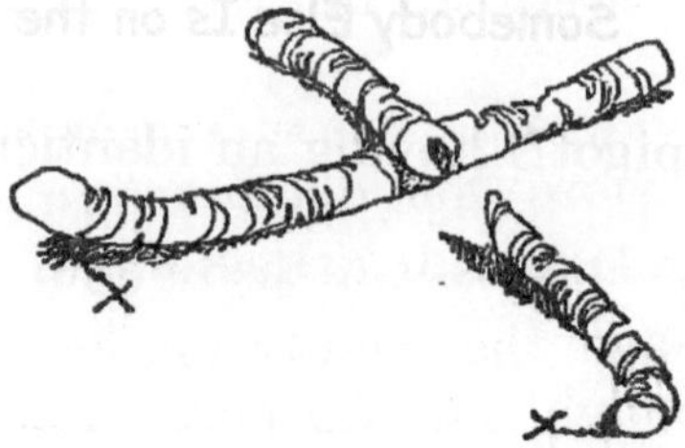

(Students of ancient legends and folklore which lingered until the present century in parts of Europe may see an interesting resemblance between a single leg of the X-drone and the worm or huge dragon which allegedly terrorized the countryside. See the writings of John Michell and F. W. Holiday.)

One leg of the X-drone is separated from the main body. At first I thought there might have been an accident, but no. The leg fits into the socket. It has clearly been an intentional separation, as though to exchange one leg for another which performs another function. Exchangeable parts on a rig 1V2 miles long!

Note the chains attached to the ends of two legs. Note at the ends of the chains the objects with high reflectivity. These small crosses—probably made of the hardest metal possible—act as maces. X-drones flail at ridges as well as spray out craters. We can speculate that they use the rock and breccia and ore which they pulverize for building material inside the Moon, extraction of metals (iron, titanium, uranium, etc.), making an atmosphere such as oxygen from metals, rocks or sand, or an as yet unspecified purpose.

Pipeline .2 of a Mile in Diameter

Coming straight out of the end of the ridge, out of a large dark depression there, is a pipe which is between two and three miles long. To help you locate it, I have sketched it below.

Several interesting features invite examination.

The conduit or pipe has a double nozzle on the end,

each nozzle (spigot?) having an identical hood. The end of the pipe is a bit lower than the part coming out of the mountain ridge. This would make possible gravity flow.

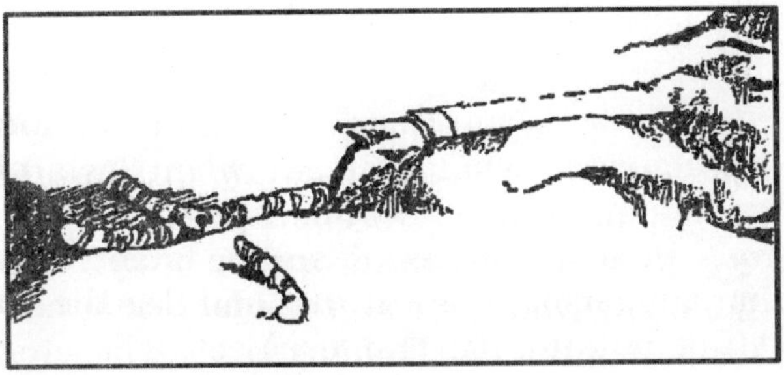

Notice that something is falling in a steady stream out of one nozzle directly onto one end of the X-drone. Another possible function of X-drones is therefore suggested: one allied to the spraying function. They sift or otherwise separate and treat materials fed into one end, while the "chaff" is sprayed out of the other end.

Does the very size of this operation indicate a high degree of efficiency in mining?

A Spare-parts Stand

Just in back of the large X-drone under discussion is a platform, or stand, of equivalent size. It looks like this:

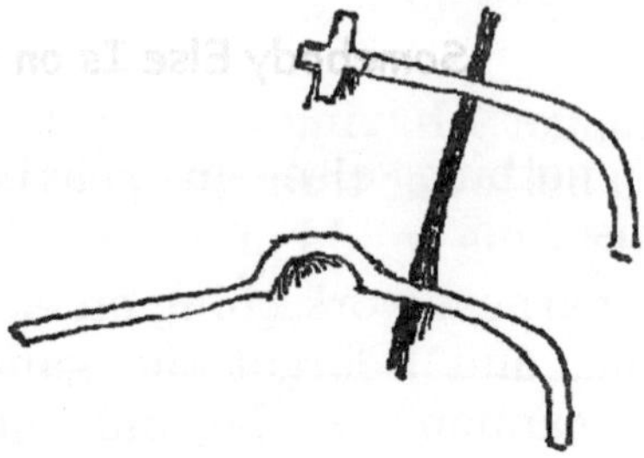

This illustrates what I meant when I said that the oddities began to click, to jibe together. We see here long rods in a symmetrical arrangement, one with a metallic- appearing cross at the .end, the other with an interesting but unidentifiable object. The cross is the same as those seen at the ends of X-drones.

The long rods are parallel bars with identically curved legs. They are raised on the rack, or stand, perhaps because the falling of dust could obscure an object lying on the ground. The object's proximity to the X-drone is also a tipoff that its function is to supply the X-drone with extra parts.

Not surprisingly, a similar "spare parts" stand can be seen in at least one other photo. One wonders how long ago in Their history They made planned obsolescence obsolete.

Spewing Out a Filament

An old friend shows up between the comer of the ridge and the small ponding effect where the ridge ends at the right (plate 10). It was also in a photo taken by Matsui of Japan and reproduced as plate 8 in Moore's A Survey of the Moon. The object looks like an oversized cannon. In the Matsui picture it is seen spewing a filament across an expanse of crater (a very square crater, by the way) toward a similar object on the opposite rim. I was tempted to think of it then as some sort of extraterrestrial game, and the thought is still tempting; nothing else—in Earth terms, at least—makes sense.

But the earnest work going on elsewhere in that area sobered me, and I forgot the games hypothesis. The oversized cannon is beyond question one more functional rig in a complex series of steps undertaken by a complex culture. You supply a label, since I haven't enough evidence for an idea of what to call this or what its function may be.

Here is what it looks like:

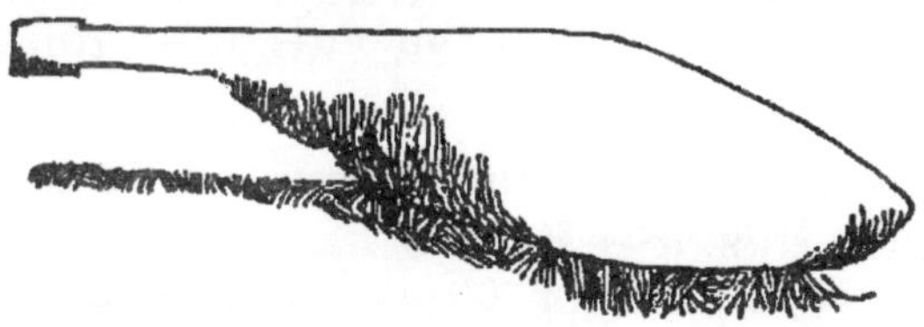

Another Mystery

There is another kind of object in the King Crater area —a new one to me—which boggles the mind. It appears in plate 12 in at least two places. It is difficult to draw because of its unfamiliarity. One cannot be sure if parts of something else are being included in the drawing or not. (If enough cases of a phenomenon are seen, the essential characteristics become familiar, and extraneous ones lose significance.) It is seen most clearly just behind the object picking up sunlight at the foot of the ridge. Here is what it seems like to me:

No Energy Shortage on the Moon

This last phenomenon concerns, I believe, power.

In several places this oblong object has been seen, always raised at the same angle, always with two knobs symmetrically located on top at either side, always with a cord or filament running from it. We have seen it connected to the super rig working on crater rim terraces.

In plate 12 on the rough ground in front of the ridge it looks like this. (See below)

Electric power. Power stored and meted out and controlled through this object. Is this what runs the X-drones? Is this what maintains and furnishes a constant atmosphere with just the right constituent elements?

This is speculation, admittedly. The only thing we can say with assurance is this: the object is manufactured. For all we know, it could be a fast-food emporium or a giant movie screen.

"There are lots of unexplained things on the Moon," the NASA scientist said. "We're puzzled."

I had gone back to Goddard to get my bibliography from the library. As usual, I'd stopped at the guard office at the main entrance to get cleared to go in. NASA says it's an ordinary Government agency without Security with a capital S, but you have to be invited by someone there if you are a private citizen. And it's amazing how many NASA employees have top security clearances. "This isn't an open installation," the steely-eyed guard said. I had to get cleared by telephone, fill out a form, get a pass for my car, wear a big sign on my lapel, get a map with directions to the one building I was cleared to visit, and carry a piece of paper for the person I was visiting to okay. Ordinary Government agency?

"But you have hypotheses," I said to the NASA scientist. "For some." Suddenly he turned to me, and there was only the hint of a smile on his face. "There are—dammit, there are some things you don't even try to communicate, do you know what I mean? Even you—even you see things you don't know how to discuss, what to say about them. They're too—too—"

It was the first time I'd examined this myself, and I knew he was right. There were things in King Crater and other places that I would not attempt to discuss. Everyone has a threshold beyond which he or she will not go. Some concepts are just too wild, too far out, with no way of knowing whether they are seen correctly or not. I stuck to concepts as safe and conservative as I could when I wrote or talked about the Moon. (That tells you where the establishment stands.)

"At any rate," the NASA scientist said, "there are hypotheses. Some."

"Such as the occupation of the Moon by space races," I said, trying to keep my voice matter-of-fact.

Pause. "That is not a viable hypothesis."

"You mean nobody thinks of that at all?"

"Individually, maybe. Privately. Seldom out on the table." He thought for a moment. I thought about the word "seldom." "We reach out for a natural explanation, you know. No matter how unlikely, a natural explanation is always preferable to a scientist. And why on Earth—on the solar system!—would any intelligent race want to be on the Moon?"

"I think they're taking uranium and titanium and iron," I said, picking three metals out of the hat because I knew they were there. "Thorium, God knows what else."

The scientist looked embarrassed. He had not admitted to the possibility of there being a They, and now he was invited to discuss the Moon on that basis.

Segments of the Apollo 17 Preliminary Science Report ran through my mind:

... All mare basalts have been found to be unusually rich in iron and sometimes rich in titanium. . . .

The orbital gamma ray experiment results show that the region north and south of the crater Copernicus is remarkably rich in radioactive elements. A band going from north of the Fra Mauro site to west of the Apollo 15 site contains soil 20 times richer in uranium and thorium than either mare or terra in other parts of the Moon. . . .

Perhaps the explanation is that the Moon is richer than the Earth in the radioactive elements uranium and thorium and that these elements are strongly concentrated in the upper parts of the Moon.

I did not pursue this theme. He changed the subject to the bibliographic search system at the library—had I gotten what I wanted? Yes, I had. The people in the library were very helpful, very cooperative. We separated. Homeward bound, I contemplated the world as it seemed to me then. A schizophrenic world. A world Kafka might have invented. Unreal ... A hot yellow sun blazing in the North African desert and some people were yelling it was raining out, there Was no sun at all. . . And pounding in the background were the words over and over "Need to know . . . Need to know . .. Need to know."

I wondered where it would end. When you came right down to it, we didn't have to know much of anything, did we? I mean, we would eat and sleep and go to work like drones without knowing what was going on in the world and the universe, right?

Oh, wow.

And Morris K. Jessup, that mathematician-astronomer who'd been way ahead of the rest of us and died before his time, asked the question nearly twenty years ago: Who has beaten us to the Moon, perhaps by hundreds or even thousands of years?

CHAPTER SEVEN
Service Station in a Crater?

Give our space agency "A" for marksmanship. The first step in this country's unmanned exploration of the Moon—· Ranger Seven—impacted the satellite on July 31, 1964, and sent to Earth as its swan song a picture which made one astrophysicist in Washington spill live pipe embers onto his lap as he studied it.

The mission of the Rangers Seven, Eight, and Nine probes was to take pictures They took seventeen thousand of them, many worth a prize in any· competition. Surveyor and Orbiter probes, programmed to soft·land or orbit the Moon, came later.

The point of impact for Ranger Seven was less than two hundred miles from Bullialdus. (In the shadow of Bullialdus, you remember, was that shocker, the enormous gear with the generator or turbine close by, in an area of high seismic activity.) The picture which discombobulated the NASA scientist showed six objects fashioned with loving skill and a mist or vapor blowing straight out of a turret·like protuberance.

I have a middle·grade acquaintance at NASA whose reaction to this is "It can't be—they'd have told me about it!" Who said, "In a society where secrecy is possible, one never can be sure of getting the truth"?

NASA said the largest object seen in the picture was a rock mass. The picture given to the press was grainy, with poor resolution. NASA also put out a bound_ volume of Ranger Seven pictures, 199 in all, taken by the F·a camera. They were about the same quality as the set of eight given to the public. The bound volume was used internally, for NASA committees. But there was one difference—and

what a difference! The last one showed a trace of detail in the sunlit portion of the crater with the "rock mass" in it.

That trace of detail was enough to stimulate curiosity and make one crave more knowledge of the crater. This is what the sunlit portion of the crater looked like in picture No. 199 of the bound volume:

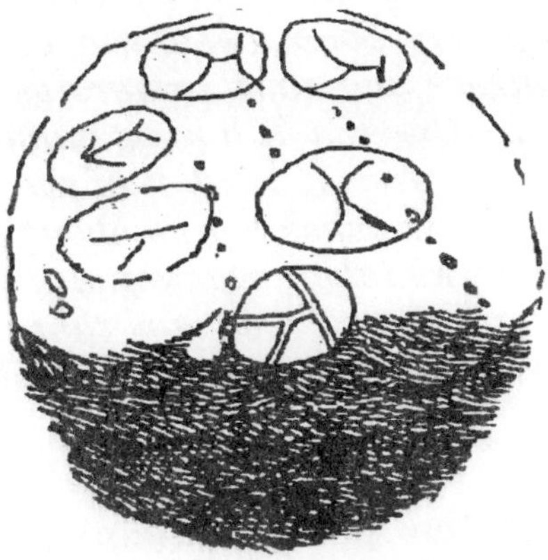

Whenever one sees a repetition of a pattern like that, one gets suspicious. But the shaded portion of the crater remained a mystery. No amount of scrutiny of the photograph would reveal much more detail, beyond two points of light and a hazy mass.

But help was on the way.

Living in the Washington area, one counts one's friends among many Federal agencies, especially after twenty or more years there. I counted as a good friend an engineer working with Goddard Space Flight Center in Greenbelt, Maryland. Goddard is part of NASA.

This engineer, knowing of my deep interest in the

Moon, brought home a photograph which had been circulated among the Goddard staff.

This photograph is a mosaic. The final pictures taken by partial-scan cameras have been superimposed on the final picture from the full-scan camera with a 25-mm lens.

The photograph was put together by the Jet Propulsion Laboratory, California Institute of Technology, NASA,

Pasadena, California. The blurb at the bottom of the photo says,

"The partial scan pictures were taken from altitudes from approximately 8000 feet down to 1000 feet from the Moon's surface and show craters as small as 3 feet across. Note in the F-a full-scan camera picture the large object in a crater at the left of the picture. This is believed to be a rock mass and is about 300 feet across. The F-a picture was taken from an altitude of 3.7 miles. The enlargement above illustrates that the partial scan pictures show surface features not visible in the F-a picture."

The part of the photo containing the crater in question with the "rock mass" is taken with the full-scan camera, which does not show the fine structure of the lunar surface, as does the partial-scan camera. Unfortunately, I was told, only one camera could operate at a time, and there is no partial-scan picture of the crater close-up.

However, the photograph issued by the Jet Propulsion Laboratory, and privately circulated in NASA, has detail enough—enough for one to suspect that Ranger Seven did not land haphazardly where it did. Enough to recall that the state of our technology permits us to program a missile to home in on any of the following, and lots more: heat, metal, radiation, water, carbon, oxygen, movement, various gases, and so forth. I believe Ranger Seven was programmed to zero in on such a target. The coincidence of our space shot landing so near to this crater with no program in mind, no sought-out objective, would be too much.

The alternative is also plausible and supports the theory. That is, craters such as this, full of artificial objects, dot the Moon. They are everywhere. (Why not? Aren't we supposed to keep our minds open?)

I am familiar with the hazard of over-reading photographs. One gets to know that "noise" in a picture can create all sorts of patterns for the lively imagination. But one also comes to realize that, while a thousand monkeys at a thousand typewriters might, in an infinite number of years, duplicate the works of Shakespeare, it isn't likely in my time. If I see even one page from *Macbeth*, I sit up, adrenalin working. *If that can't be a rock in the picture— and it can't—then what if it?*

The full crater as revealed by the two photos is sketched below. And there are some very important points to be made concerning it.

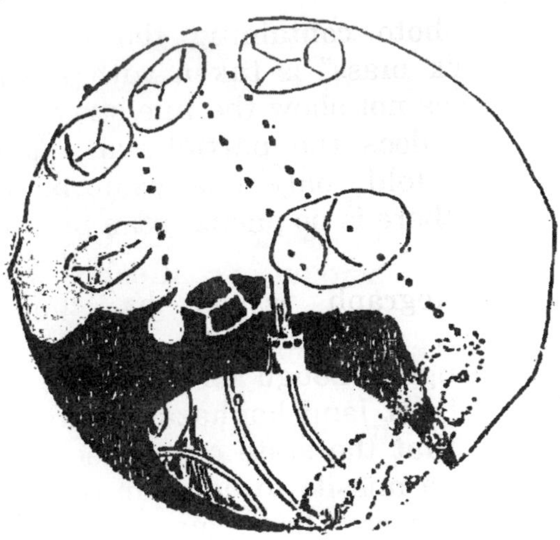

• Notice the gleaming object cutting into the shade at the center of the picture. Its configuration is identical to that of the objects in the sunlit portion. In the Jet Propulsion Lab photo (mosaic), the object appears to be either intrinsically illuminated or raised sufficiently to catch the sun.

• The large object in the shaded area catches the sunlight, but not with the same high reflectivity of most rocks and crater rims. It appears to have a dull metallic finish. The object is smoothly rounded, symmetrical, and has what appears to be a turret-shaped protuberance, which is also remarkable for its perfection. There are three marks almost at the end of the "turret" which are evenly spaced apart and at a constant distance from the edge. The eye picks them up as bolts, rivets, or design. The end of the "turret" is curved, exactly in the way that the end of any pipe or cylinder appears curved when you look at it slightly away from the plane of its great circle. A mist or vapor appears to be blowing straight out of the end of the "turret." Curved lines girdle the large object on its left portion. Two of them are perfectly parallel. What kind of rock looks like that?

• There is a mist, dust, or something similar across the lower right quadrant of the crater, through which details can be seen.

• The gleaming object cutting into the shade in the exact center of the crater is touching another gleaming object, shaped like an electric light bulb. One could speculate with a fair amount of confidence that the oval object with the gleaming Y on its back is somehow being serviced by the other object.

• The object in the upper left of the sunlit portion is perhaps similar to the others but too indistinct to be seen as one.

• The Y marking on the back of the gleaming object cutting into the shade is identical to that on the three objects along the upper rim of the crater, and somewhat similar to that of the fourth. A review of all the world's alphabets reveals that this Y with a line beneath it is similar to an ancient Semitic Z found on the famous Moabite stone and dates to 900 B.C.; and to an ancient Karosthi Z. Karosthi is an adaptation of the old Aramaic alphabet, thought to have been used by Jesus, to the needs of the Indian languages. But pursuing this line of thought leads perhaps to the notion that current occupants of the Moon helped Earth's populations make the history of the Old Testament and Vedas times. From that to the idea that the Bible and the Vedas were UFO stories . . . No. Best forget that z altogether. It's simply the "tree of life" ... or a "y" with a line beneath it . . . and who knows what else?

Space Ship

The objects in the sunlit portion of the crater are about 150 to 200 feet in diameter, judging by NASA's estimate that the large "rock mass" is 300 feet across.

The design on their backs reminds one of the markings

on a landed UFO in New Mexico seen by a police officer. One report indicated that what the officer saw resembled the following sketch.

The direction of the frontal arms is reversed. Outside of that, the similarity is striking. Reported size, also, is in the same ballpark. The conviction grows that when one looks into that crater near where Ranger Seven impacted on July 31, 1964, one is watching space vehicles take their turn in getting whatever it is they need: a recharge, their unique mixture of life-maintaining air, food, a mechanical overhaul. . .

Or could it be that this is not a service station, but a parking lot outside a main entrance to an underground city! The mist/vapor/cloud or whatever it is escaping from the "turret" is most interesting. One thinks of being on the roof of a large apartment building, where there is a vent for the air conditioning and heating system. Or in the back of a restaurant where the stale air and kitchen odors are blowing out. If there is a community below that crater, there would have to be a continuous supply of new atmosphere, and venting' out of the old. (I know, I know, my mind is closed. I am attributing to them the same need we have to breathe.)

There are several other photographs which show interesting or amazing things in small craters. We will come to them in later chapters.

Why is so much of the intelligent activity on the Moon associated with craters?

Much of the evidence of engineering seems to be in craters, particularly the very large ones. Although there are startling examples of architecture and sculpting of mountain masses, the "manufactured object" kind of evidence is not found in such high frequency at ground level. The business of working and living seems to go on inside craters.

There has been speculation on the part of some scientists that a trace of atmosphere, such as heavy gases, may exist on the Moon, and build up in the bottom of craters and other low places. The extension of this argument would be that They exist on this atmospheric trace. However, we know enough about the Moon now to know this it not really true. An atmosphere would be detectable, because light is dispersible in air and the crater shadows would not be seen as so dark. There are numerous other objections to this theory, not the least of which is the fact that atmospheric traces were not detected by our astronauts, who had myriad detection devices.

But this is not to say that mists, vapors, gases do not exist at all on the Moon. They exist as by-products of the intelligent activity there. We will read more about these strange mists and gases in later chapters. Some of them are colorful and move about slowly. Others just seem to hover, as the mist in the lower right-hand quadrant of the crater featured in this chapter seems to do. And then there are the kind which behave exactly as any gas or vapor blowing out of a tube should behave!

There are other amazing features of this crater—features which show its kinship with others. For example, there are symbols above ground nearby. (These and others will be covered in Chapter Fifteen.) There is a suggestion that the mist in the lower right-quadrant may be forming in order to hide from view what is underneath. "Operation Cover-up" is a common theme on the Moon. Sometimes, in examining closely a particular patch of ground, one gets the feeling that everything seen is camouflage, fake, sham; that the Moon's occupants do not wish us to see. the surface for what it really is.

I ran across Sam Wittcomb in Dallas. He was attending a symposium, and I was on public health business.

I asked him, "You say that some scientists doubt the natural origin of that crater and its contents?"

"There are discussions about it," Wittcomb answered. "As you know, Dinsmore Alter in his book said it was 'controversial.' I've talked to one person who would stake his life on the artificiality of all the contents. The official NASA line is that it's a rock. I sometimes think they split along disciplinary lines. You must see this problem of interdisciplinary communications in public health."

"In spades," I had to agree. "You say that some within NASA believe that an intelligent non-human race is responsible for what we see there?"

"Yes."

"What about the purpose—"

"That is another matter. Any answer must be rank speculation," he continued, "although one of Their purposes certainly seems to be mining. You can be absolutely certain that the three people outside your door are strangers. You can describe them, relate what they do as they await your response to their knock, but you will have no idea, perhaps, as to their purpose."

I was getting impatient to discuss my findings. "You're aware of the big rigs They seem to be using to push the ground and craters around?"

"Shockers! I wondered how long it would take you to find them! I assume you're talking about the large X configurations. They alone have convinced more equivocal scientists than any other feature," he said, confirming my feelings.

I went on, "Getting back to that crater near where Sanger Seven crashed—I know you don't know what's going on there. But could you say what the best guesses are? Is there a consensus shaping up?"

"No consensus," he answered. "I've heard someone say that the metallic-looking object in the shaded part of the crater could be an entry to an underground community. Others go further and call attention to its resemblance to Earth's baby subs, bathyspheres. We've lost an awful lot of seagoing things, you know. You've heard about the strange disappearances?"

"Who hasn't? How about the objects in the sunlit portion of the crater. Sam? Any guess on those? They look like spacecraft to me, parked there to get serviced."

Wittcomb smiled. "Presumably."

Then he said something that made me want to fly back to Washington that night and attack the NASA photo tubs the first thing in the morning. But I was sobered by the amount of work relating to the Moon still to be done.

"Take a look at the pictures of Mars sometime," Sam said. "Especially the two moons. If you think our Moon has inexplicables—"

"I've glanced quickly at the pictures," I said.

"Take another look. There's an opening in one shot that had to be built. It looks like the mouth of a bottle. Don't forget that the two Martian moons weren't discovered until the 1870s—soon after the crater Linne disappeared from our Moon. Those shots of Mars have some of the analysts at NASA standing on their heads and going without supper."

And did you know that in 1955 General Douglas Mac· Arthur said, "Our next war will be an interplanetary one. The nations of the world will have to unite against attack by people from other planets"?

CHAPTER EIGHT
Things That Move Around

It was one of those not-for-credit summer courses, infested with educational tramps, and the old building had no air conditioning. A bull session course in astronomy without the math and the tedious hours of observing. The discussion on how to identify intelligent life on a planet from a distance away started irrelevantly, and continued after the hour was up. By then it was an argument. Two or three students believed that an extraterrestrial race might be beyond our comprehension.

The instructor got badgered into taking a poll—an inane idea, of course, but I am sure he did it only because he recognized that the need of the adults in the class to be entertained and kept out of mischief was greater than their receptivity to education. "You are skimming the surface of an alien planet," he said resignedly. "What are the three leading factors or things which could lead you to the conclusion that the planet holds intelligent life?"

My wife found the notes to the course recently: mildewed, barely readable. On the last page were the results of the poll. (Pages 94-95)

The "Miscellaneous" category included such gems as "evidence of litter on the landscape."

It proves nothing, and means little—except that the last item, "agriculture and/or herding," is the only factor we have not seen on the Moon. And "signs of vehicles moving around" (I would change this to "signs of creatures, vehicles, etc., moving around on the ground") is the only other factor appearing on that list which we have not yet considered in this book. (The rays, of course, are evidence of aboveground flight.)

And evidence for ground movement is overwhelming.

"Intelligent Life" Factors	No. of Responses
Architectural or geometric construction	19
Evidence of change not due to weather	18
Signs of vehicles moving around	15
Lights not due to volcanoes, etc.	9
Repetitious signs, signals, writing	9
Agriculture and/or herding	8
Miscellaneous	8

Apollo 17 and Boulder Tracks

I first became interested in Things Which Move Around by studying a photo from the Orbiter series. The photo showed long tracks from objects which ostensibly had rolled down the hill. NASA labeled them boulders.

Occasionally another photo came to light which had a long track of a moving object in it, but my interest did not peak until the Apollo 17 Preliminary Science Report came out in 1973.

Thirty-four tracks in the Apollo 17 landing area were measured and investigated. Length of the tracks ranged from .1 kilometer to 2.5 kilometers, with an average length of about .75 kilometer. Track widths ranged up to 16 meters (about 38 feet), with an average width of over 18 feet.

Most of the objects to which the tracks were attributed were wider by 20 to 30 percent than the tracks themselves. The tracks were found in clumps—that is, eight or ten would be in one cluster on a slope, perhaps a dozen or so in another cluster, and so on.

I was intrigued. Twenty men or more with long crowbars would be needed to dislodge even the smallest of the boulders. One wonders if a large bulldozer would have had much effect on them. When the boulders were dislodged, a fantastic additional force would have been required to keep them moving on a 25-degree slope. A picture of one of the huge boulders which "rolled" down the hill is shown in the

report. Its angularity would not be conducive to rolling; it is practically oblong. And it is big as a room.

NASA admits in the report that the cause of all the rolling is not known. There is one more significant and interesting fact: Of the thirty-four boulder tracks studied, a causative boulder could be located , in only eight cases. In the others, there was either no boulder or too many to definitely indicate the culprit. Did boulders actually make the tracks?

Objects Which Move Uphill

Plate 14 (67-H-1135) shows two long trails, 900 feet and 1200 feet long. The objects obviously making the trails are light-splashed by the sun; no real detail can be gleaned from studying them. But they do not look like boulders.

"Do you know how much force it would take to set in motion a rock seventy-five feet across? Volcanic action might do it, but we have NASA's word for the fact that the Moon (on the surface, at least) is seismically quiet.

The smaller object in the photo—the one making the longer trail—came up out of a crater before it continued down the hill. Repeat: It came up out of a crater.

There is a fascinating tread mark on the trail of one of the "boulders." There is also a symmetrical design on the "boulder" itself.

Two-Bumped Objects with Interconnections

Plate IS (67-H-758) represents either an edifice (i.e., intelligent construction for living or working), a vehicle, or a form of life.

This statement must be made, regardless of its disturbing nature. It is not enough, nor is it truthful, to simply say that the picture is "interesting." It is beyond the realm of possibility for the objects in it—showing the characteristics they do—to be of natural origin (i.e., not made or grown).

My interpretation of the objects in plate 15 is below:

The bigger objects in the center cluster all have two symmetrical bumps at the highest edge which appears at six o'clock in the picture. The shadows follow the contour of these bumps and accordingly turn out to be double points. Several other NASA photos contain these double-bumped objects, clustered together, having the same properties as these.

There is an interesting distance relationship among the objects; for example, note the relationship between the outer objects—6, 7, 8, 9, 10—and the inside cluster. They are roughly equidistant from the inside cluster's mid-point. And note that the outside objects are all single-bumped and are spaced like sentinels.

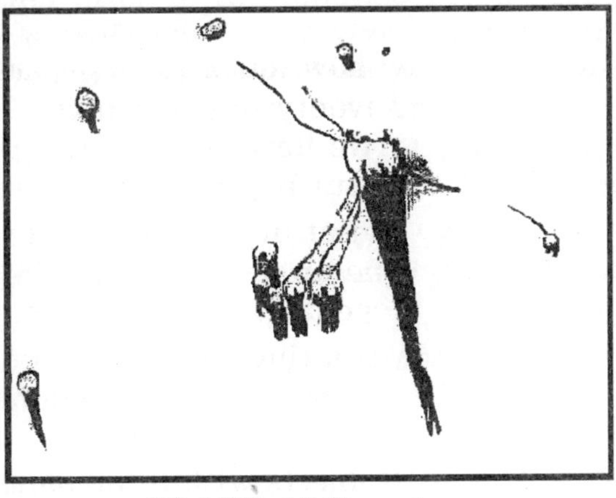

PLATE-15 Drawing

There are clear markings running from the largest object, 1, to all but three of the others. These markings could be tracks, or they could be conduit lines for life-sustaining atmosphere, or they could be for communications. (In other NASA photos showing similar two-bumped objects, there are clear ground markings looking as though the objects moved around.)

Objects 1, 2, 3, and 5 have smoothly rounded appendages or buttresses, each in the front left, although not

positioned exactly the same. All of the objects having appendages and bumps at the top are facing in the same direction.

Something interesting is taking place between objects 5 and 4. Could it be sexual contact or communications?

Looking at the photo with a reading glass reveals a fantastic sight. For example, the bumps which resemble eyes on 1,2, and 3 are ^11 facing in the same direction—to the right. It is as though sensor devices (animal or mechanical) picked up the spacecraft going overhead. (The spacecraft probably reflected the sun against a black sky so it could be easily seen.)

This photo was given as a handout to press services by NASA and was reproduced in newspapers with such cute expressions and labels as "Christmas Trees on the Moon!" (referring to the long pointed shadows which dominate the picture). Which shows the level of reporting in this country on Moon matters, and the level of public interest about the most serious problem facing humankind today. The Russians considered these objects definitely artificial, and presented 'a picture of a model and analysis of their geometry in the Russian publication *Technology for Youth.*

This photo so intrigued me that I made a special trip to Goddard and NASA headquarters in an effort to find out what the official thinking was.

That the objects are a kind of edifice seemed to me

less likely than the other alternatives. I had come a long way from the time when my close associates accused me of having an "edifice complex." But nothing could be ruled out. The fact that there were markings on the ground, however, made me favor the possibility of vehicles or forms of life. Constructions would not move around, and permanent constructions would be more likely to have connecting cables underground, where they could not be cut by meteorites.

Vehicles, on the other hand—while they might well have connecting cables—would make more pronounced tracks and would probably not be built in so many different sizes with odd appendages. This is strictly opinion, of course— we have no right to inflict our values of design on the occupants of the Moon.

More than one clue points to these objects as being a form of life or a mechanical substitute for life: the appendages, the varying sizes (function of age), the groupings, the "eyes." However unlikely an answer, and God knows it's unlikely, it still must be considered a viable one. An even more unlikely answer would be boulders.

Carl Sagan had postulated that a layer of carbonized matter could be below the surface of the Moon. Moore and Wilkins had said it was possible that a form of life totally different from anything we know could be on the Moon; and they meant indigenous life.

At NASA, the people with whom I'd talked in the past said they were familiar with the photo. Did they have knowledge or a theory as to what the objects were? No; speculation was not their business. The photo was interesting; that was as far as they would go.

Sam Wittcomb was available on the second try.

"Read the back of the photo," Sam said after I'd set the stage and asked the question. I put down the receiver, got the picture, and then read it aloud over the phone. He stopped me when I got to this sentence: "The striking shadow casting protuberances shown are naturally occurring features on the lunar surface."

"I think I see what you mean, Sam."

"It may be a clue. Indigenous life would, after all, be 'naturally occurring.' "

"But it also says the biggest one is fifty feet wide at the base, maybe as high as seventy-five feet!"

"Ever see how big a vine on this planet can get?" Sam asked. "Or a boa constrictor? How about the reptiles in the Mesozoic period?"

"Okay," I said. "And the gravity of the Moon is so little, it might support a larger mass."

"Now you're thinking."

I was thinking that it was a preposterous idea that life could develop on the Moon, in spite of the photo and what Wilkins and Moore said and Sam's willingness to include it as a possibility. I was thinking it was preposterous because most everyone said it couldn't be true, and because indigenous life on the Moon would mean practically any old chunk of planet circling a sun in the universe had a fair chance of having a kind of life of its own.

And it was preposterous because it meant that the intelligent races on the Moon which had moved in from other places were (seemingly) letting that indigenous life—if it existed—go on living, and not killing it off for Lebensraum or meat or excuses to kill called sport. Intelligent beings just weren't supposed to behave that way—if you went by our experience.

Plate 16 (67-H-510) shows long trails of objects which "rolled down the hill." It is fascinating because it pairs one of these objects with a two-bumped object. The one which rolled down the hill leaving a trail is too light-struck for us to see whether it has two bumps or not. But it is the same size as the one which does.

A sharper look at the photo reveals that another two-bumped object is nearby, less than an inch (in the photograph) from the other one. This one has a trail (or other kind of ground marking) parallel to the major trail left by the "rolling stone." Two rolled from one direction, one from the opposite direction. Which rolled uphill?

We have in this photo excellent presumptive evidence for suggesting that the "rolling stone" is a two-bumped object; that two-bumped objects abound on the Moon; that external or internal forces—most likely the latter in view of the directions from which the objects are coming—can set these objects moving; and that they are either vehicles or forms of life.

Tracks of moving objects are too numerous to catalogue fully. One moves in a sweeping circular motion up the slope of a ravine; another moves sideways on the slope; a third shows no track at all, but a raised filament on the ground connects it to a fourth. Most of the objects are classic two-bump. In some photos the objects are clustered together in'"families," and in at least one photo (e.g., the floor of Copernicus) the objects seem to have clustered on rises where the sun is hitting. Most interesting is the similarity between objects which seem to move around—i.e., leave tracks—and those which have two bumps and appendages.

A New Kind of Engineered Object

Plate 2 has objects which appear different from the two- bump-with-side-appendage kind. They are perfectly oval. One of them is striking for its engineered aspect. It is in a cluster of other objects. It looks like this. (Page 101)

This is the .manufactured object I told you about in

Chapter One. It, more than any other single feature, forced me to organize my findings and write this book. And that was before I'd known about the craters being sprayed out!

The three "struts" at one end of the object, with the peak at the opposite end, are so perfect as to demand the conclusion that this is artificial. My guess is that it is a vehicle of some kind.

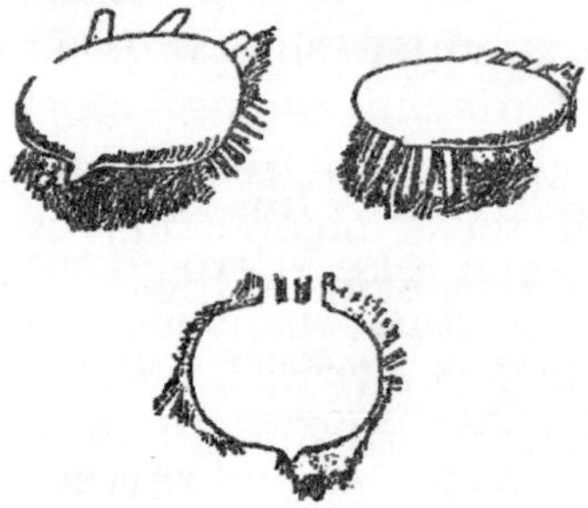

It is absolutely impossible for this kind of regularity—the perfect oval, the evenly spaced rear struts, the perfect peak—to be produced on a random Moon by nature. (Note, incidentally, the presence of several "cilia" or thin appendages pointing downward on the right side.)

In Chapter Ten you will read about the kids in the Young Astronomers' League who asked the Administrator of NASA why his employees did not communicate the really interesting things seen in the photos to the American people. This is a good case in point. The object I have sketched above could not possibly have been missed by trained analysts. Every oddity referred to in this book has been seen by them. How simple and helpful it would be to add a paragraph on the back of each photo calling attention to the oddities seen and what the thinking about them is!

The fact that current thinking about phenomena may be inconclusive makes little difference. Prior to elections the ultimate winner is inconclusive, yet the voter is barraged with opinions, discussions, and polls. Too, there is nothing conclusive about the etiology and cure of coronary-artery disease, yet opinion as to prevention and diet and management is presented in the media daily. One could go on and on with examples.

When is it safe to come to a conclusion? When everyone finally knows about it?

Vehicle Perched in a Crater

Plate 17 (67-H-327) has a crater which confirms things we've seen elsewhere, and comes up with a startling new feature of its own.

Let's first discuss the more pedestrian features of the sketch following.

The outer rim of the crater is actually a hexagon. But the arc-like intrusions from twelve to five o'clock constitute parts of a cover; these anomalous craters can be covered over completely, and we have seen them in various stages of the process.

Note the edge of the lintel protruding from just below the rim at nine o'clock. The bulge outside the rim underscores its presence. This lintel is probably one of the horizontal poles which can shoot across a crater to support a cover.

The climax is the object perched just inside the rim at four thirty. It looks like a diving bell on legs. There are resemblances to our spacecraft. (There were no manned or other landings in this area.) The object which I believe to be a vehicle is sketched on page 103.

Elsewhere in the photo, not pictured in my sketch, are objects similar to the two-bump-with-side-appendage oddities seen so frequently elsewhere.

We have seen a variety of objects which make trails on the ground, sometimes uphill, across flat ground, everywhere. One special type has two bumps and a single appendage; a confederate usually seen with it has one bump and is smaller. Another type is circular or oval with a peak on one end and three struts, evenly spaced and similarly sized, on the other. And we have located an object which bears a startling resemblance to some of our Moon-landing vehicles. The trails that these objects leave are sometimes in the form of a tread-like pattern. Trails are seen going down twenty-five-degree slopes with boulders up to fifty feet

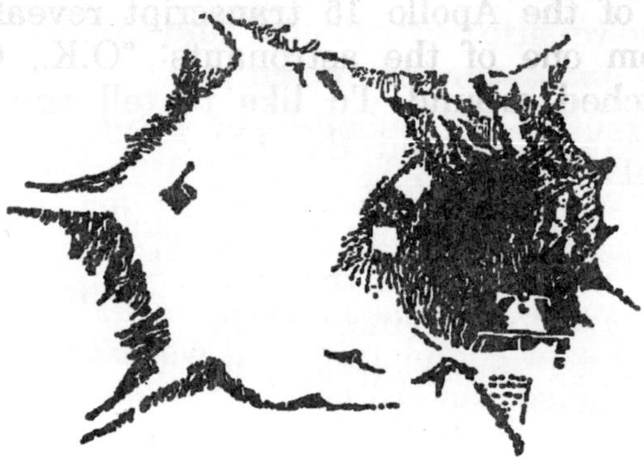

wide nearby. These trails are officially attributed to the boulders, but in the majority of cases NASA was not able to pinpoint which boulder had made the trail. The weight and size of the boulders cast serious doubt on the hypothesis as given in the *Apollo 17 Preliminary Report*, that natural forces ("Material buildup on the uphill side . . . erosion on the downhill side . . . cyclic thermal expansion and contraction . . . impact [of meteorites] . . . seismic events . . . impact-induced ground motions") could have set these boulders in motion; most of them are angular, square, or oblong. We are left with the knowledge that some strange things happened, and happened in clumps.

We have only touched the surface of the whole

subject of things that move around on the ground. The floor of Tycho and certain other high-activity areas of the Moon show so much ground disturbance that it is virtually impossible to sort out the tracks from lava flow and general ground wrinkling.

Later in this book you will see the profound evidence for things which move around above the ground: lights which move steadily and rapidly in the inky blackness above craters; white rays deposited around craters; and the well-documented observations of flying objects leaving and returning to the Moon.

A reading of the Apollo 15 transcript reveals this quotation from one of the astronauts: "O.K., Gordy, when we pitched around, I'd like to tell you about something we saw around the LM. When we were coming about 30 or 40 feet out, there were a lot of objects—white things—flying by. It looked like they were coming—it looked like they were being propelled or ejected, but I'm not convinced of that."

Clearly, "things" move around by many modes of transportation on and above the Moon.

And Arthur C. Clarke has this to say in First on the Moon (Little Brown and Co., 1970): "Even if 99% of the Moon is completely sterile, the existence of small 'oases' with microclimates of their own, is not wholly out of the question. . . . It would be a great mistake to assume that any life forms that have managed to survive on the Moon would be primitive. . . . Who can say what may be lurking in the rugged foothills of Tycho, among the 30,000-foot-high peaks of the Leibnitz Mountains, or in the vast, drowned crater of Tsiolkovsky, which dominates the far side?"

CHAPTER NINE
Rays Streaming from Craters: A Startling Theory

The Moon is a strange place—still strange and mysterious, notwithstanding the U.S. Ranger, Orbiter, Surveyor, and Apollo flights, and at least 32 Soviet Lunik and Zond Moon probes, unmanned but including Moon landers, orbiters, and return missions. There are still countless puzzles as to the Moon's origin, its contents under the crust, the nature and purpose of its occupants, etc.

Not the least of these puzzles are the white rays which stream from many craters in all directions. Some of these rays (e.g., from Tycho) have been traced for 1500 miles or more. Others are short. There are rays so wide that they cannot be singly distinguished but form a mass of pure white around the crater; others are narrow, like a chalk line. Nobody knows how they got there.

You can be sure there is no lack of theories. In the end, though, most astronomers and astrophysicists concede that they are mysterious. The purpose of this chapter is to take the mystery out of these rays.

Properties of the Rays

Whenever one proposes a theory to explain a phenomenon, he must be certain that it covers all examples. We must list all known properties of the rays;, we must describe all types; and only then can a new theory be compared with the list to see if important areas are covered or left out.

(1) Rays do not appear to have sufficient depth to cast a shadow.

(2) They are white, and do not show up well under oblique sunlight (i.e., when there are pronounced shadows). On the other hand, the rays become very enhanced under full midday sun.

(3) Rays typically cross the darkened smooth maria, ridges, mountains, and valleys with no interruption. Where they stop suddenly, there is usually another crater at that point. While most rays are reasonably continuous, a few can be found which stop, start again in a few miles, stop, and start again.

(4) There are some "over-systems" of rays, notably the system of crossing rays from Copernicus, Kepler, and Aristarchus.

(5) Some rays do not emanate from exactly the center of a large crater, but are tangential to it.

(6) There are many examples of craters which have pronounced rays coming from one, two, or three directions only. More than one crater can be found with a single ray streaming from it.

(7) Many rays (e.g., from Copernicus) seem to end in a tiny white craterlet.

(8) Rays range in width up to ten miles.

(9) They appear to consist of dustlike particles which are perfectly spherical, judging by their appearance from all angles, and which cling to everything touched.

(10) They seem to have the same albedo (reflective quality) as white rocks from inside the Moon's crust.

Textbook Theories as to the Origin of Rays

Velikovsky, that insightful genius who confounded

the orthodox scientists with his Worlds in Collision, was, of course, vilified in return. But he had the sense to admit that the rays were a mystery, and did not create an explanation merely to explain all phenomena within the context of existing knowledge. He said, "Bright streaks or 'rays' up to ten miles wide radiate from some of the craters; their origin, too, is not known."

All observers are not as cautious. The Flammarion Book of Astronomy supposedly put the matter to rest with these words; "When a crater is formed . . . dust is flung out in all directions. The particles describe long parabolic jets in the vacuum, their length being enhanced by the fact that the lunar force of gravity is 6 times smaller than on the Earth. They fall to the ground and form long rays diverging from the crater. The halo's of the fine recent craters Tycho and Copernicus can be seen in a small telescope; the rays are a fine white and stretch to considerable distances."

Fred Whipple, in The Nature of the Moon (·3rd Edition, 1968), writing from the vantage point of more experience following several Moon probes, makes a statement which may be in accord with the old orthodoxy but clashes violently (as we shall shortly see) with the observations of the Apollo 12 astronauts: "The huge rays from the great new craters such as Tycho cannot, however, be explained by white dust alone. The U.S. Ranger VII pictures have confirmed Kuiper's telescopic observation that the rays are rough and rocky. White rocks, such as appear in the Surveyor pictures, could cover the surface of the rays sufficiently to keep them relatively white for long periods of time until they were slowly covered by debris thrown from more distant parts of the Moon. Their increase in relative brightness at full Moon, however, requires further explanation."

The extent to which scientists will go to protect (a) the orthodoxy and (b) one another is astounding. Whipple's statement reveals his concern over the fact that dust from whatever sources is always falling on the Moon, and even if it is only a few particles a century over a given area, in time—and time is what the Moon has had plenty of—a surface whiteness would become obliterated. If you assume that the rays were caused by splash-out from meteoric impacts, or volcanic ash thrown up and out, or a whiteness showing through cracks in the Moon's surface resulting from alternate heating and freezing, then you must have an explanation for the fact that they still show white and get even whiter during a full Moon.

Suffice it to say that, while a few astronomers have flatly stated that they did not know the source of the rays, most have been content to accept the easy (but unscientific) explanation that splash-out from either meteorites or volcanic eruptions has been responsible.

It's time to talk sense.

Why the Old Explanations Cannot Be Correct

A meteorite hitting the Moon and making a crater would tend (unless it were a very oblique hit) to create a ray pattern all around the crater. There are as many craters which have only partial ray systems as there are those which are fully patterned.

An oblique hit by a meteorite would not create a single ray. The splash-out would be more general over the direction of flight.

I have sketched below a few good examples of odd ray systems around some craters. These ray systems are not peculiar to small craters or to large craters; they occur in all sizes (e.g., craters of half-mile diameter on up to many miles in diameter). (See below)

Another strong consideration not examined in the books I have read is that of overlapping ray systems; a new impact would, if this theory is the true explanation of rays, tend to partially obliterate another nearby ray system. But this is never the case. All rays seem to show up clearly, even in the case when three ray systems, from Copernicus, Kepler, and Aristarchus, overlap.

A good selection of ray types can be seen in a single photo (plate 18 [69-H-28]). Two overlapping coupled ray systems, a single ray, feathering, a ray stopping at a crater- let, and the whiteness of the crater bottoms are all visible.

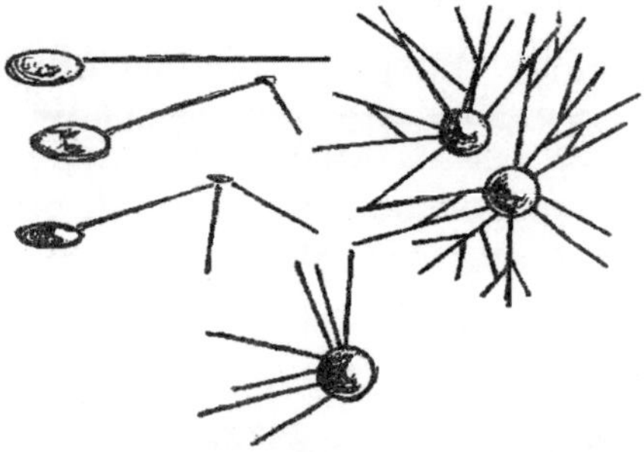

One of the most striking arguments against the splash-out from meteorite or volcanic-ash theory is the fact that the rays do not always stream from the center or the main body of the crater, but sometimes from a point tangential to it. Dinsmore Alter in Pictorial Guide to the Moon (Crowell, 1967) writes:

"A simultaneous study . . . will show many peculiarities in the ray system of Copernicus. One is the fact that the major rays are not radial to Copernicus. The second is that in Mare Imbrium, north of the crater, there are many plume-shaped short rays which are radial to Cogsmicus. The points of the feathers are toward that crater. In a few cases a craterlet is observable on the pointed end of such an elementary ray and in nearly all cases a brightish spot can be seen there that can be assumed with some confidence to

contain a craterlet. Examination of the two major rays extending northward into Mare Imbrium shows that they have a complex structure. Despite overlapping, there are places where this structure can be observed as composed of the elemental plume rays, which are radial although the complex rays are not." [Italics added.]

Let's pause to think about it. Does the above statement give you a clue? Consider what the basic properties of the rays are, consider what they cannot be, and then consider the prime thesis of this book. Can you guess what the startling new theory for the crater rays is going to be?

A New Explanation for Crater Rays

We have seen clearly thus far in this book that intelligent, purposeful residents are on the Moon. We have seen results of their efforts, as well as indications that they are there now.

It is probable—although admittedly there is no solid evidence for the following statement—that the Moon has been occupied for a long, long time, perhaps thousands upon thousands of years.

How do the occupants of the Moon move around? The answer to this question lies in the area of common sense. Suppose they arrived on the Moon from another point in space by spaceship, perhaps powered by a means totally unknown to our scientists at the present time. By extension, They move from one point on the Moon to another by spaceship. In some of the photographs of the Moon there are objects which may well be these spaceships. They range in size from smaller than a football field (e.g., the objects seen in the small crater near where Ranger Seven impacted the Moon in 1964) to a mile or more in diameter (e.g., the objects suspended from the side of the cliff in Tycho). Readers batting an eye at this size estimate are referred back to the early pages of this book, to the references by some scientists to the fact that we may be looking at the artifacts of extraterrestrials without recognizing them, and especially to the comment by the Canadian scientist about mental straitjackets.

It is but one step now to the new explanation for crater rays. Flying objects on the Moon land at the bottom of big craters having a fine, powdery white dust at the bottom. They go back and forth to other craters, to deliver or to get a supply of something. The fine, powdery white dust sticks to the underbellies of the flying objects. As the flying objects vibrate above the ground, the dust gets shaken off. Because the flying objects have definite places to go, the dust tends to fall as straight rays along certain paths. In the case of very busy craters, the occupants in the flying objects have many places to go in all directions. In the case of some quieter or more specialized craters, there may be interchange only between that crater and a single other point on the Moon—hence one single ray.

Admittedly, this explanation is tied to Earth-person's perception of commerce. But no explanation based on natural phenomena fits, and we know from visual evidence that objects come and go in the craters. And we shall shortly see that any object landing in these white-bottomed craters must pick up a white dust which is then subject to being shaken loose.

I searched the NASA literature for reference to the rays and for new data on them. I talked with Dr. Farouk El-Baz, the geologist who had been so closely associated with the Apollo flights. He confirmed that the rays consisted of a fine white powdery dust or soil. He referred me to the preliminary scientific report from the Apollo 12 flight. This was a manned landing on the Moon.

I quote from that report:

"The material [at the ALSEP deployment site] appeared to be loose and fluffy and, according to Astronaut Bean, was difficult to compact by merely stepping and tramping on it. [i.e., the material constituting one of the white rays of Copernicus]. The fine-grained surface material had a powdery appearance and was easily kicked free as the astronauts moved on the surface. During the Apollo 11 EVA [i.e., "extravehicular activity"], Astronauts Armstrong and Aldrin noted the ease with which fine-grained material was set in motion while they were walking on the lunar surface.

The tendency of the loose, powdery surface material to move easily in the lunar vacuum and 1/6 gravity environment imposed operational problems that were augmented by the fact that the same material also exhibited adhesive characteristics that resulted in a tendency for the material to stick to any object with which it came into contact. As a consequence, equipment and spacesuits became coated, and housekeeping problems arose from the dust brought aboard the LM at the conclusion of EVA periods... .

Fine-grained material adhered to the astronauts' boots and spacesuits, the television cable, the lunar equipment conveyor, ALSEP components, astronaut tools, sample return containers, the color chart, and the cameras and camera magazines....

It appears that under the shirt-sleeve atmosphere (5 lbs. per square inch pressure) of the command module, the fine, dusty material lost its adhesive characteristics."

Those who hypothesized that the rays streaming from craters consisted partly of boulders were wrong. Those who guessed that the rays shone from cracks in the Moon's surface were wrong. The rays are simply a thin covering of white powdery soil which sticks to everything—including the underbellies of flying objects.

This explanation is totally in accord with the properties of the rays as we now know them. Flying objects would not necessarily emanate from or return to the center of a large crater—hence, rays which are tangential. Flying objects may well make many stops in their travels—hence, "feathering" of the rays and streaks which sometimes connect two major rays.

The white streaks go right across rilles, ridges, valleys, mountains—as white dust falling from a flying object would. Raymond A. Lyttleton points out in The Modern Universe (Harper, 1956) : "And there are the strange bright streaks, some ten miles or so broad, that extend out from many of the craters but have no perceptible shadow effects and must presumably be an extremely thin superficial phenomenon. They also run right across all other irregularities without any resulting change in color or width."

I think it is clear to the reader that crater material splashed out in an arching curve at time of impact or volcanic action might be terminated at a high mountain range; whereas a flying object, progressing in a generally straight line and shaking off white powder, will create a continuous ray much as we see crossing mountains and valleys alike.

The most convincing aspect of this new theory is that it accounts for the brightness of the rays after millions of years of space dust slowly accumulating on the Moon. The large craters, such as Tycho and Kepler and Copernicus, which have the largest ray systems, are probably, in Patrick Moore's words, "Pre-Cambrian [i.e., over five hundred million years old], in which they are at least as ancient as the oldest terrestrial fossils." They may perhaps be considerably older. The Apollo 17 Preliminary Science Report infers from the data that "The time of formation of more than 90% of the cratering on the Moon was 4 billion years ago or earlier." (They must, of course, be aware of the craters currently being made by "spraying out"!) The fact that the white powdery soil can be seen today with such brilliance can probably be attributed to a continuing process, that of countless trips made by many flying objects over countless years, rather than to an impact in the Pre- Cambrian or earlier times.

An interesting sidelight on the Apollo flights to the Moon—after several manned landings, thousands upon thousands of photographs, samples of soil and rock—is that the great mysteries of the Moon have come no closer to solution. We still do not know the origin of the Moon, the cause of the craters, the nature of its core. Fesenkov and Oparin in *Life in the Universe* (Twayne, 1961) write, "*Despite the enormous development in the last decades no new explanation of the formations on the lunar surface has been advanced. The so-called meteorite theory of the formation of lunar craters, first proposed by ..Gruithuisen in 1824, is still seriously debated today.*"

One can search scientific reports of the Apollo flights in vain and still not find a serious inroad to these mysteries. Patrick Moore admitted in A Survey of the Moon, written prior to the manned Moon flights, that "*The plain unwelcome truth is that we are still very much in .the dark. as to how the Moon's, craters were formed.*"

In the same book he states clearly how much of a mystery the rays are: "*The Moon is full of puzzles, but it is probably true to say that the most baffling problems of all are set by the bright rays. Not even the most casual observer can overlook them when the Moon is near full, but so far nobody has been able to find out precisely what they are.*"

Astronomers of the world, this chapter is offered for your consideration.

And now that ice have contemplated myriads of flying objects ceaselessly going hack and forth over the Moon, lugging, ferrying ... it may be worthwhile to wonder what C. G. Jung meant when he wrote (Flying Saucers, Harcourt, Brace and World, 1959): "These rumors, or the possible physical existence of such objects [i.e., UFOs] seem to me so significant that I feel myself compelled . . . to sound a note of warning. . . . My conscience as a psychiatrist bids me fulfill my duty and prepare those few who will hear me for coming events which are in accord with the end of an era ... I am, to be quite frank, concerned for all those who are caught unprepared by the events in question, and disconcerted by their incomprehensible nature ..."

CHAPTER TEN
What's Going On in Tycho?

A late September thunderstorm moved in. We struggled to get the three reflecting and two refracting telescopes inside. It was a.simple room in the basement of a church with a long table and several chairs—that was all. Nine restless kids whooping it up, wanting action. Nine kids, sixteen years old and younger, bright kids who'd formed the Young Astronomers' League and stuck me with the task of guiding them.

In my briefcase I had twelve copies of the magnificent shot of Tycho taken by the cameras of Orbiter V during the summer of 1967. There was also plenty of paper, pencils, and reading glasses.

"The weather's socked in for the evening," I said. "Let's vote on what we do—an indoor project, or go home."

The project I had in mind was complex. I held my breath. But the abilities and energies of children always amaze me. Nine hands went up. They voted for a project.

"I have a photo of Tycho for each of you. Remember, it's about fifty miles wide. You know it has the biggest ray system on the Moon. Probably it's one of the three most interesting craters on the Moon. I'd like you all to imagine you're on a committee"—groans—"and you're charged with studying the crater and writing a letter to the Administrator of NASA, our space agency."

"But what are we supposed to tell him?"

"Whatever you agree on."

"What are we supposed to see?"

"You're not supposed to see anything. It's an interesting picture with lots to talk about. If you agree on doing the project, then take the evening to study the picture, and you can write the letter next time we meet."

Nobody wanted to go home. The four girls and five boys enjoyed being together. They'd studied the rings of Saturn and the moons of Jupiter, and knew a lot about our Moon. They tore into the project with enthusiasm.

Except one boy I'll call Larry. His father was a physicist for the Federal Government, his mother a chemist in a different agency. Larry liked discovering grape-cluster universes in space and other sky wonders, but when the conversation turned to speculation about the two tiny moons of Mars or the "bridge" in Mare Crisium, he got derisive. Now he was silent, not looking at the photo, not jabbering with the others about the sharp detail in it. There was just the faintest touch of a cynical smile on his lips.

He caught my eye.

"My father wants to know if you believe in blond Venusians giving people rides in flying saucers."

The other eight were not listening. They were too busy dividing Tycho into quadrants and assigning two kids to study each one.

"Not if he means the books by George Adamski and Howard Menger. But it's not important what I believe, Larry. We're trying to get at what you think."

"I think this is a waste of time." He laughed and looked around for support. Sometimes he was a leader in the group, because he was the oldest. But now the others were occupied. He got up. "I know what you want us to find: little green men, bug-eyed monsters. I gave them up when I was ten."

I expected him to leave. But instead he stood in back of two kids examining the photo with a reading glass. I waited for more challenges, but they did not come.

Larry wandered around the table, looking for an easy way to enter the group, but failed. He sat down at the end of the table with a photo and tried to muster a cynical smile again. I walked to his side.

"Here's a reading glass, Larry. Who knows, you might find the picture interesting. Some very important scientists have."

Minutes passed with little talk. The kids who'd been assigned the quadrants from six to twelve o'clock got restless. Larry got up and talked to somebody in a low voice. I could not hear what he said. Twenty more minutes passed. Soon three kids were clustered around him. They talked excitedly. I walked out of the room to get a drink of water. I stayed by the cooler as long as I could. When I got back, Larry was sketching something on the blackboard. He told them to concentrate on the twelve-to-six- o'clock quadrants. The cynicism was gone from his face. Now there was only curiosity and purposefulness.

At the end of an hour and a half, they were still going strong. They broke the right half of the crater into smaller pieces and assigned them out for analysis. This time Larry got a chunk. At ten thirty, the usual quitting time, they showed no signs of getting tired. A parent's car honked in the driveway. Another parent stood silently by the door.

We agreed the project would continue next week. Three days later, I got a call from a mother, one I'd never talked with before. Her voice was incredulous.

"What's the secret? She's been working on your project all the time she's not eating or sleeping. She should do her homework like that."

I felt on the defensive. "My purpose wasn't to have them work at home—"

"Don't apologize! It's great—beats TV. You should

hear the phone calls back and forth."

When we met again, the kids had Tycho worked out as far as they could take it. And without being steered—I didn't want to do that. Most of them had done work during the week. They'd met in small groups, once eight of them together.

They had questions. I tried to answer objectively. It had to be their thing. A young eye, other things being equal, is better than an old eye—their minds were less cluttered with prejudices. They already knew about light and shadow and the tricks they play and the difficulty in analyzing ground seen through a lens or in a photo. They began that second meeting composing a letter to the Administrator of NASA, and if a camel is a horse put together by a committee, the first draft of that letter looked more like a weird mythological creature.

But they knew it was bad; they backed off and groaned, then retreated to individualism. Larry took over and rewrote it to cut out the rambling and duplication. Somebody else sharpened the fuzzy thoughts, and another kid tried his hand at making it sound as though it had been written by one person. Finally, a girl took some of the testiness out of it, and when the evening was over they had a letter which wasn't too bad. I asked them to sit on it for another week before sending it; They agreed heartily.

Two weeks later they mailed the letter, with an attachment in which they described the phenomena they saw. The letter, exactly as it was sent, read as follows:

Young Astronomers' League of Rockville
Rockville, Maryland
20850
October 20, 1973

The Honorable James Fletcher Administrator

National Aeronautics and Space Administration
Washington, D.C.

Dear Sir,

On August 16, 1967, Lunar Orbiter V took a picture of the crater Tycho. We think this is one of the most beautiful photographs ever taken. The work which went into Orbiter V and taking this picture must make you feel proud.

But all you did was have this picture stuck in a big tub with thousands of other pictures. You did not tell the American people anything about the picture (except for a few technical things like where Tycho is on the Moon and where North is and how Tycho is considered to be young by scientists).

It has been six years since this picture was taken. (And other pictures of Tycho, too. One of us called your News Office and found out there are some other .pictures of Tycho, taken on different days, and they are bigger than the eight by ten we have been looking at. These pictures are in your Space Science Data Center at Goddard. The man in the News Office said we could go out there and look at them if we called a day in advance and said what we wanted to look at and then went to the Guard Office first to get a visitor's pass. We might make a field trip there.) Your employees have probably been analyzing, the pictures. You can do an awful lot of analyzing in six years. Especially when you have all that money to hire analysts. You probably have a lot of them. Somebody told us that Goddard Space Center is a lot bigger than the National Institutes of Health in Bethesda. That really rocked us because NIH must be almost a hundred years old.

There is a lot to tell the people about Tycho. It is not

an ordinary crater. There are things on the ground built by some pretty good brains. At least as good as ours. There are things that look like letters of the alphabet and even though they might not be our letters they certainly can be read by someone. There are these big coverings and things that might be space vehicles and lots of constructions that the people of our country might find interesting. We are going to tell you about these things in a separate attachment. We know your employees must tell you about them but we are going to tell you anyhow, just in case. But the people you hire to study the pictures must be a lot smarter than we are. At least about looking at pictures of the Moon. If they are not, and they do not tell you about what they see in the pictures, why did you hire them? Are we right that part of your job is to tell Congress and the President what the Moon is like?

We asked all our parents what they paid in taxes last year. The total of nine families was $82,873. We think that all this tax money and because we are citizens of the USA means we should have more than just a picture stuck in a tub. We think every picture should have a page attached to it saying what your analysts thought was interesting in it. This would not cost a lot of money at all. How can we have a government of the people, for the people, and by the people unless you tell us what our tax money is really going for? Is your agency working for us or for its own benefit?

One of the boys in our club says you do not have to do these things. He wants us to put in a sentence about his minority report. He says you do not have to, tell us what is in the pictures because you have a big engineering job to do. You had to put a man in space and then on the Moon and then you had to put spacecraft even further out to the planets. This boy thinks you did a great job in these things (the rest of us do too) and you do not have to turn into a bunch of desk people. He thinks it is up to the writers to report to the people about what is on the Moon and somebody is fluffing the job.

But there is this other boy in our club whose mother works at the National Cancer Institute and she says there is no such thing as doing research or engineering development (except for secret weapons) unless you tell the people what the results are. She says she has to write research reports all the time about her work.

All the stuff she writes can be read in scientific journals and other places. But when it's really important you can read it in the daily newspapers and magazines. The rest of us think she is right.

We hope you will think about this and maybe start telling people about what your employees see in the Moon pictures.

Sincerely yours,
[Nine signatures]

A week later, Larry and I were adjusting the spotting scope on a six-inch reflector and had a chance to talk.

"I think that business about the bug-eyed monsters, remember? And the blond Venusians? Well, it—it wasn't fair."

I listened.

"You can make anything look silly if you try hard enough. If you pitch enough curves." He tightened a thumbscrew and thought for a few seconds. "A few nights ago I saw this old Western on TV. There were these guys, they were selling colored water from the backs of wagons, pretending it would cure a million diseases."

"They called them quacks," I said. "Old-time medicine men."

"Yeah. Quacks. But suppose every time someone mentioned medicine, I started talking about quacks."

"That would be pitching a curve," I said.

"And if someone talked only about the mistakes doctors make—"

"Obfuscation," I said. "Obscuring the real issue, which is not the small percentage of mistakes. If there's a circus lion loose in town, you can count up all the alley cats and

show that ninety-eight percent of the animals seen were plain old cats."

"I get it," Larry said. "Obfuscation. Two percent of them is still a lion. Nothing can change that."

The kids got back a PR-type response to their letter a couple of weeks later: "Thank you for your interest"—that sort of thing. They put it on their bulletin board, annotated with their comments, and that was the end of that project. Except that my faith in the young eye and brain was bolstered, and Larry and I became good friends.

The photo of Tycho is shown as plate 19 (67-H-1179). Below are the phenomena reported to the Administrator of NASA by the kids. The drawings are mine. I dropped two of their features as being questionable.

(1) The feature which first caught Larry's eye, the one getting first billing in their letter, was the octagonal covering with a glyph on it. (Glyph: Symbolic figure or character intended for communication, incised or otherwise carved or depicted.)

It is sketched below. In the photo of Tycho, it is on the inside rim at about two o'clock.

It is clearly an octagon, and appears to be a covering, with long polelike objects sticking out from under the

Edges.

There is a startlingly clear glyph on it. The symbols should not, however, be linked to our letters; simple glyphs representing intelligent communications from widely disparate civilizations would no doubt have overlapping and similar constructions.

Running straight across the octagon from corner to opposite corner are three barely perceptible ridges, giving the impression that a cover material has been stretched tautly over horizontal poles.

(2) Moving down the rim, we come to a long wide section which is totally artificial. Not one square inch of the high-albedo section of rim (roughly a tiny bit above three o'clock) is natural. It looks like this. (See below)

Note the left edge. Although superficially rough, there is a design to it and an overall straightness. The right edge has some interesting objects which seem to be suspended from the artificial rim. Note the perfect scalloping on the edge of one of the objects.

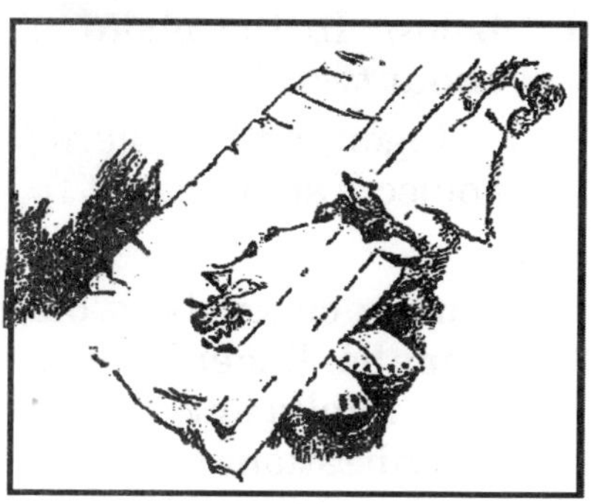

To the right of the oblong section of rim is an obviously constructed cylinder. Markings at either end are evenly spaced.

(3) On the bottom inside rim is a large area which duplicates the phenomena in the Lubinicky-Bullialdus area. Description is difficult, but it is obvious that they are manufactured. The bottom Tycho rim looks like this. (See below)

The possibility that this structure represents solar-energy mechanics should not be ruled out. The huge ovals could be flat panels soaking up energy and transferring it to apparatuses which convert it to electricity.

The oval objects in both instances cited thus far have cilialike protuberances spaced at even distances on the underside.

The portions of arc seen are absolutely perfect segments of circles or ovals. There are evenly spaced "nodes" on the rims of the objects.

This bottom rim section is where most Lunar Transient Phenomena (LTP) are seen in Tycho. NASA has a chart showing where the most prominent LTP-flashes—flares, glows, obscurations—are seen. Exactly in this section is an X on that chart.

(4) There are several hemisphere-shaped coverings. One prime example is on the right-hand edge on a level

with the octagonal covering. There is another directly behind it.

My first inclination (and still a strong one) was to accept these as being natural occurrences: swelling of the ground from magma eruption, volcanic action, or freezing. There are domes formed naturally by one or the other of these actions. The kids picked these "hemispheric coverings" up right away, and I just as quickly rejected them for inclusion in this chapter. But some detail in one of them gave me pause. They look like this. (See below) Magma swelling would result more probably in a shape like half an orange laid flat. These objects, judging by the light and shadow, are more like a quarter of an orange.

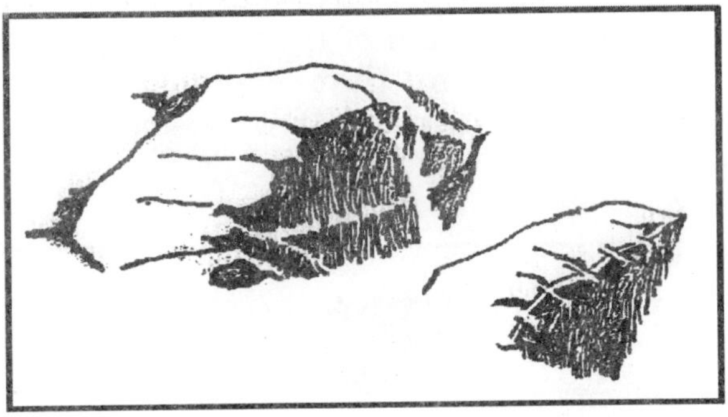

The object on the right has a cross weave going around its edge. There are two possibilities here, both indicating intelligence: the coverings are artificially created; or the ground was pushed up through natural means, thereby exposing an artificial weaving or matrix already on the surface.

(5) NASA provided a blowup of the highlands area to the north of Tycho (plate 20 [67-H-1651]). A most remarkable object—one we shall see several times in different parts of the Moon—showed up. The object is

always tilted at the same angle, it always has two nodes on the top, it always has a "cord" or filament leading to something else. (Is the bell-shaped object flying? One cannot tell.) Here is my rendering:

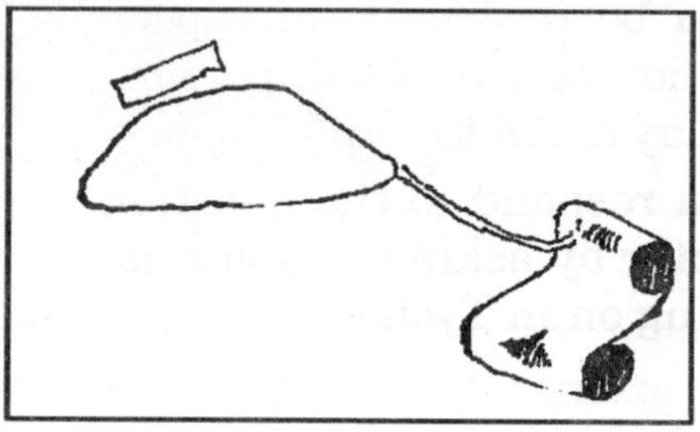

We close with an object which brings smiles to the lips of the most conservative people. It looks like a miles-long screw (plate 9). This configuration can theoretically result when lava is forced through a spiral opening. But the location of this screw, beneath broken crust, casts doubt on that explanation. Also it is interesting that a dome-like construction sits on the crust nearby.

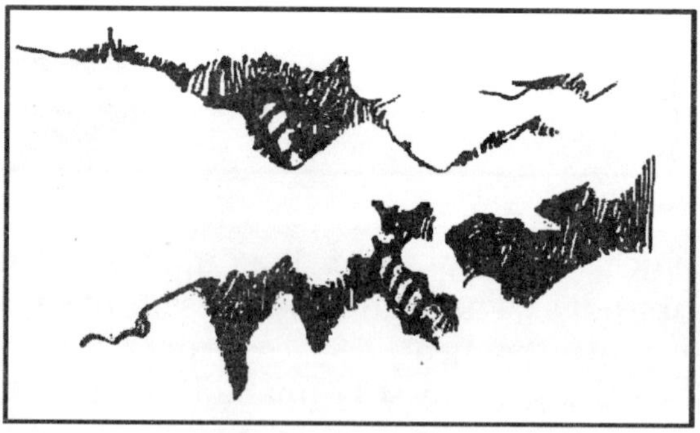

Screws could be used to hold together parts of the skin of the Moon. They could be used to pry up the crust—a lever of sorts., They could be examples of exposed underground constructions. (Remember: there is evidence of vast destruction on the Moon—even more than from meteoric impact. Whatever else the occupants of the Moon are doing, certainly two of their functions include "Operation Salvage" and "Operation Cover-up.") Other uses can be imagined. The occupants may even be reserving an especially large "screw" for presentation to any Earth-person mustering up enough nerve to lay claim to "our" Moon.

We can respond to the question posed by the title to this chapter by asking another question: "What, in fact, is not going on in Tycho?"

And did you know that Lenin once said: "All human conceptions are on the scale of our planet. They are based on the pretension that the technical potential, although it will develop, will never exceed the 'terrestrial limit.' If we succeed in establishing interplanetary communications, all our philosophical, moral, and social views will have to be revised"?

CHAPTER ELEVEN
Gas Jets on the Moon

How much atmosphere does a being with a mechanized body require?

Humans breathe in a mixture of nitrogen and oxygen with some carbon dioxide and argon added. Traces of helium, krypton, neon, xenon, and moisture lurk here and there. The amount of nitrogen is nearly four times that of the oxygen.

We exhale a lot of things, including carbon dioxide: wastes from the blood. If we had a colony on the Moon living in a pressurized dome with the right mixture of air in it, there could be a purifier system which would rechannel clean air back into use after treatment. But in the long run there would still be waste gases to be expelled.

If the occupants of the Moon breathe an atmosphere kept in a vault underground, a vent would be required to eject gas under pressure. Whenever this gas is ejected, some distortion or obscuration of the Moonscape will take place. How much depends upon its level of impurity and temperature.

Industrial activity implies gas ejection. Methods for making alloys—known or unknown to us—almost beyond doubt require melting of metals, a process which creates gases. Any kind of smelting or manufacturing process which makes use of fire will create smoke, carbon dioxide, carbon monoxide, etc. A highly advanced technology will probably still have uses for processes involving high heat. A thousand years from now, we will probably still have to break eggs to make an omelet.

Obscuration of the Moonscape is one of the prime

"transient phenomena" studied by NASA and university scientists. NASA has documented nearly a thousand cases of LTP, of which a good percentage involve haziness or fuzziness where part of a crater can be seen with crystal clarity and another part is distorted. Most authorities believe these obscurations, distortions, and hazes are caused by escaping gases. I agree with them.

But where we part is this: the scientist authorities who state their position or opinion invariably attribute the phenomena to natural gases escaping through a fissure in the Moon's crust. I believe much of the phenomena to be caused by purposeful ejection of waste gases.

I have seen gas escaping in three places on the Moon— that is, three places where I can be reasonably certain that gas ejection is taking place. There are hundreds of major and minor obscurations to be seen in the NASA pictures, and through the telescope, but I do not include them as gas-ejection cases, because the specific venting point is not seen. When I look at such a hazy spot in a picture, I cannot be certain that it is not a defect in the photography or in the developing.

But in the highlands area north of Tycho there is a remarkable seven-mile-square neighborhood. It can be seen in the standard Tycho picture, plate 19, but with no detail at all. NASA made a high-resolution photograph of the northern highlands; it is plate 20. A small area of the standard Tycho photo seems to have been blown up at least three or four times, and with startling clarity.

The seven-mile-square neighborhood is alive with construction and activity. I was looking for something else when I stumbled upon it—true serendipity! Below are some of the splendid creations to be seen in this relatively small area. One interesting point to be made about these areas of construction and activity on the Moon is that the surrounding areas are so different. Ordinary, natural Moon rubble looks just like rubble and can be mistaken for nothing else. Construction by an advanced technology stands out vividly and also can be mistaken for nothing else.

As in the Lubinicky-Bullialdus area, the occupants here and inside Tycho favor the hemispheric covering and constructions which abut each other and almost fit like jigsaw puzzle pieces. I would say that if different races occupy the Moon, the same one (the same culture, same physical type) resides in both these spots. It is worth pointing out, too, that both are on the near side of the Moon, in the southeast quarter, perhaps four hundred miles apart.

But the really striking feature in this area is not the constructions, which are so numerous on the Moon that a large atlas would be needed to note them all. The feature which made me whoop like a Prince of Serendip is gas being ejected from two places, gas which distorts or fuzzes the background view and which blows out of discreet points (nozzles? smokestacks? vents?). It is clearly ejected under pressure. It goes straight up, does not fall over in an arc, as would water or a solid, and has the cone-of-dispersion appearance which a gas ejected under pressure should have. Its dispersion becomes complete when it is lost in the vacuum of the Moon.

There are two other suspicious cases of gas ejection from discreet points, but they are not sufficiently clear to be certain.

The better of the two clear examples looks like this:

Those who wish to examine this neighborhood firsthand may find this phenomenon in plate 20, approximately two inches from the bottom, exact center. The gas and constructions can be seen with the naked eye, but a reading glass helps.

This, incidentally, is another example—and we will see many in this book—where photos taken at a different time but under similar lighting circumstances would beyond question show clear-cut change. It is unlikely that the gas ejection continues all the time. Lunar Transient Phenomena feature just that—transience. If the gas ejection is a result of industrial activity (which I believe it is, as opposed to the excretion of used atmosphere), then there must be times when the smelters shut down, the fires cease. Then another picture on another day, treated the same, blown up the same, would show no gas ejection.

There are other neighborhoods of construction and activity in this remarkable picture. One is on the extreme right-hand edge, two inches from the bottom. The geo-metricities there are even more striking. And at the bottom middle of the picture is a beautiful example of "ribs" on the Moon: those parallel filaments which almost appear to be strengtheners, heavy rods forming a cover. A person with a vivid imagination might even conjecture that the Moon was "built" a long time ago, in another corner of the universe, before all hell broke loose.

And Arthur C. Clarke says in his Voices from the Sky [Harper and Row, 1965]: "Dr. Shlovskii's stimulating theory [i.e., that a moon of Mars is hollow] appeals to me because some ten years ago I made an identical suggestion concerning the innermost moon of Jupiter. In a story called 'Jupiter V' I pointed out certain peculiarities of this satellite and developed the idea that it was a giant spacecraft which, ages ago, had entered the solar system and then been 'parked' in orbit round Jupiter while its occupants went off in more conveniently sized vehicles to colonize the planets."

CHAPTER TWELVE
Stitching Up the Moon

An hour with Farouk El-Baz, the geologist and research director, kicked off what was going to be an unusual day. In a third-floor loft above the National Air and Space Museum's gift shop, he continues some of the same work he did for NASA: interpreting the surface of the Moon.

Some of the objects and Moon features I discussed with him he saw the same way. Others he did not. He recognized immediately my sketches of the coverings pulled over large areas. I was pleased that we saw some of the objects on the Moon the same way, although I realized that if I had pressed him for his interpretations, some would probably have differed from mine.

When I got back to my office, near Dupont Circle, an old friend called. He is an information officer for one of the many divisions in the Department of Health, Education and Welfare. This friend, whom we shall call Lew, attended two meetings of the National Capital Astronomers' group and immediately became an expert on the universe.

"Got a tip for you," Lew said.

"Let's have it."

"There are twelve moons of Jupiter. Four of them are big, and you can even see them with binocs. The others are pretty small."

"That's a great tip," I said, arranging the message on my desk, "with apologies to Galileo and Barnard and others. Except there are now fourteen known moons of

Jupiter."

"But there's more to the story! Four of the moons go the opposite way from the movement of their planet!"

"The eighth, ninth, eleventh, and twelfth," I said. "They call it retrograde movement."

"That's it!" Lew said, getting excited. "Now tell me how in hell a moon can have a motion in the opposite direction from its parent body!"

"There are other satellites in the solar system with a retrograde motion, Lew."

"You haven't answered my question."

"I was getting to it. You know as well as I do what the theory is. The satellites were captured by the planets."

He laughed. It was not an amused laugh. "I was waiting to hear you say that. Captured, my foot! For a planet to capture a moon would mean the asteroid coming just close enough at exactly the right speed."

"But it's possible," I said.

"Sure," Lew said. "And it's possible to drop a football from a jetliner into a trash can in front of Grand Central Station. You know damn well those moons going in the opposite direction from the planets are artificial!"

"I don't know anything of the sort, Lew. Not as long as it's possible for them to be captured in a natural way."

We ended the conversation. I felt queasy. It was easy to be a staunch defender of the conservative view: defend the faith, defend what is. Let nobody attack successfully. Use cute smiles and put-downs where useful. For the next hour I had a difficult time thinking of anything else. I remembered that the four retrograde moons of Jupiter (unlike the others) have enormous angular inclinations from the orbit of the primary planet. All four retrograde moons (unlike the others) are between 13 and 14.7 million miles out. All four have revolutions (unlike the others) of 600 to 700 days. They are all small, like the moons of Mars.

I shoved the work on my desk aside and called Lew back. I told him about Phobos, the inner moon of Mars, which goes around the planet three times while the planet is rotating once on its axis—a very strange, theoretically impossible situation. We started to communicate.

Later in the afternoon I called my wife. She'd gotten home early from teaching. I asked her to get the letter which had arrived a couple of days earlier from Dr. Witt- comb. The hotel he was staying at had slipped my mind. After the crackling of paper, she said, "He'll be at the Mayflower. He says you can call him there if you want." "I'll stay downtown."

"I expected you to say that. Did you see his P.S.?" "Something about tailors." I'd been nonplussed then—and intrigued. She read it to me: "Did you know the Moon has giant tailors?' My goodness! Is it a joke?"

"A very serious joke," I said. Sam had told me on his last visit that he'd have interesting leads for me regarding current activity on the Moon. He came in contact with a lot of people associated with the space effort in his work, and when he heard something interesting he often passed it on to me.

At five thirty Sam had not arrived. There were too many planes due that evening from the Coast' for me to guess which one he'd be on. I crossed Dupont Circle as the red and blue and yellow lights up and down Connecticut Avenue were beginning to show through the evening haze. Coming toward me, past the Old Stein Restaurant, was a human wreck. He looked eighty but was probably fifty, wore a ragged coat with the stains of a thousand short- order meals, and had rheumy eyes. I usually saw him up around Q Street. As he shuffled beside me, I gave him the customary quarter. All the way down Connecticut Avenue I kept thinking about the time since Homo sapiens was first on Earth, the hundreds of thousands of years spent learning how to grow things and build shelters and solve problems—all kinds of social and technical and personal problems—and there, at the pinnacle of all those thousands of generations of struggle and learning and evolution, was this rheumy-eyed man with my quarter.

I wondered when and how the occupants of the Moon had solved these kinds of problems.

Two martinis and a chunk of prime ribs later I'd purged myself of pseudo-philosophy, and when I next tried for Sam Wittcomb at the desk of the Mayflower, he was in. He met me ten minutes later in the lobby. He'd been champagned and dined so much on the flight that now all he wanted to · do was walk and talk. We went down to Pennsylvania Avenue .because he liked the symbol of the White House even though the people didn't always live up to it. We continued down Fifteenth Street to the Mall and past the old Smithsonian. I had a happy image of sitting in on a long talk between El Baz and Wittcomb, an honest talk about the Moon as it is, not as it's falsely represented.

"You're going to hear Harrison Schmitt, of course."

"Why? Where?"

"He was the first Harvard man on the Moon. And the first scientist. Aren't you a Harvard man?"

"Don't hold it against me," I said. "Where's he speaking?"

"National Aviation Club, lunch tomorrow. The Harvard Club of Washington co-sponsors."

"I'll go," I said. A Harvard man on the Moon could tell a lot. Schmitt had been on Apollo 17 and is one of the brighter young men in NASA, with a Ph.D. to boot. In a chauvinistic mood, I told myself that you don't graduate from Harvard unless you can observe keenly and report clearly.

For a minute I actually forgot that someone up there

with a science teaching post claims you can make UFOs in a bottle. Another scientist at Harvard took the lead in a vendetta against Velikovsky in the early fifties, blackmailing a publisher by threatening to withdraw his textbook business to prevent publication of Worlds in Collision. It was ultimately brought out by Doubleday, which had no college-textbook division. You win some and you lose some.

We tired on Fourteenth Street, headed back toward Pennsylvania Avenue, and caught a cab. I asked him what he meant when he said the Moon had giant tailors. For a few seconds he was silent, staring at the White House bathed in floodlights.

"You see a lot of wreckage on the Moon," Sam said.

"Agreed."

"The wreckage could have taken place a thousand years ago or millions of years ago."

"Right."

"One argument the people use for the occupation-eons- ago theory is just that: many of the artifacts we see are part of the wreckage. It's easy to believe there were aliens once on the Moon—aliens who left."

"So what's—"

"Hold it. What if there-was visual evidence that the aliens had been doing repairs, stitching up the broken cover of the Moon, pulling big pieces together—and they weren't finished?"

"It would seem logical, then, that they're still around, still repairing," I said. "Where is it?"

"Several places," Sam said. "I'm surprised you haven't found them. Someone in the Jet Propulsion Lab sketched some out for me. But I'd already known of them there."

I wanted to know the person's name, but Sam blew

the whistle. "Wouldn't be fair. He'd never trust me again. He's sensitive about being identified with these ideas, just as I am. Just as Sagan and his peers, who don't talk publicly, are sensitive. Science is not only a harsh mistress—it's tyrannical, too."

We got out of the cab in front of the Mayflower. A Congressman I recognized was walking out with a tall, beautiful redhead. He was on a committee concerned with NASA appropriations. I had an insane urge to buttonhole him right there on the sidewalk and make a case for funds so NASA could put another team on the Moon in more strategic places than before. The urge passed quickly, praise God. Sam said, "I'll give you a clue to where the stitches are. Have you found evidence of change yet?"

I had to confess I had not; none that I could be certain of.

"Then I'll give you a clue on that too. Try King Crater. Be back in a couple of minutes."

He came back with his briefcase, and we repaired to the Town and Country bar to drink Chivas Regal. Neither of us could tell the difference blindfolded, but it sounded good.

"The stitches are in the Bullialdus area/' Sam said. "You know the photo?"

"Lubinicky," I said. "And A, B, and E craters. I've worn out two prints of it already."

"You're fond of the area. But frankly, you haven't seen but a fraction of what's going on around there." -
"So show me."

"I think you should discover them, for yourself. Look carefully in the rubble between the craters, and then check what you see with what's "in this envelope—but don't open it until you've really studied the area."

I promised I'd play it his way.

"Look for splits in the top layer of the rubble," Sam said. "Splits showing shadow below. Look along the lines of the splits. There's a second place the stitches can be found: Tycho. You've seen the blowups?"

"Six evenings in a row," I said, jotting down what he told me.

"You're looking for stitching. I mean that literally. Things laid across the rent in the skin, holding the edges together. Almost like the crosspieces in a zipper, only longer and farther apart."

We killed our Chivas and got up. He looked tired.

"Call me if you like between six and seven tomorrow evening," Sam said.

"You'll be at the Aviation Club to hear Schmitt?"

He shook his head. "Be tied up all day at Naval Research."

A minute later I was on the street alone, wondering if it all had happened.

I got home in time for the Channel Four news. My wife was in bed. I got out the pictures of Tycho and Lubinicky_ and set them up with paper, reading glass, and a pencil on the game table in the living room, under a strong light. Before they got to the weather, I'd located what Sam and the man in the Jet Propulsion Lab had seen. I. opened the envelope, and it checked out. I felt like Balboa and Salk and Fermi, even though others had been there before me.

These are some of the best examples of stitching the skin of the Moon in the Bullialdus-Lubinicky area (plate 3[72- H-1387]):

You cannot fail to note the precise regularity of the stitches. They are of identical length, identical distance apart, identical width. There are areas of the Moon which I now understand better as a result of seeing these examples of stitching: areas in which the gap is completely closed but where you can see the regular progression of the ends of the stitches going up on either side where the gap once was.

No, the Moon had not been abandoned after the cataclysms. The aliens, whoever They were, had stayed or come back to repair it, and the odds were They were still there. And when I found the change that Sam said was there on the surface of the Moon, there would be further proof. The evidence was piling up: the light flashes and the obscurations and the rigs working inside the craters, and now the stitching up of the skin.

All macroscopic. All showing They had licked the gravity and power problem, so They could lift almost any weight and carve a mountain into any shape They wanted.

There was a substitute host for Johnny Carson, so I shut off the TV and went to bed. The last thought I had before falling asleep was about a matter which had been pecking at the back of my mind for half an hour. I recalled the big constructions in prehistoric times on Earth; the stone slabs weighing a hundred tons or more each; the transportation of mammoth objects for long distances when there'd been no overland transportation on Earth.

Were They the same?

I went to the National Aviation Club as close to twelve thirty as possible and got the last seat at a table in view of the speaker's dais. With me I had an article by Joseph Goodavage in which he quotes some of the astronauts' chatter recorded as they orbited the Moon or walked on it. While I chatted with my tablemates, I was seeing in my mind's eye the words of Harrison Schmitt as quoted by Goodavage: "I see tracks—running right up the wall of the crater." Dr. Farouk El-

Baz had stated that two flashes of light from the moon's surface had been sighted by Ron Evans and Jack (Harrison)' Schmitt on Apollo 17.

Two by Harrison Schmitt. Goodavage got the quotes right from the original tape transcriptions. In the transcriptions were references to constructions, domes, tracks and other phenomena. I settled back for an interesting pitch by a man who'd been there.

Schmitt talked for about ten minutes on the age and geology of the Moon, all high-school-textbook stuff. I could not believe what I was hearing. A man trained as a scientist, a man who'd made many revolutions around the Moon and walked on it, and he was telling us things we could get from any neighborhood library or our adolescent children. After a couple of minutes on energy problems (he was then director of energy programs for NASA), he ended and invited questions.

Three times I wrote down questions I wanted to ask, and three times I put the piece of paper back in my pocket— too timid to risk being out of step with the tenor of talk in the room. The questions on oil and solar energy and related issues droned on. Schmitt was articulate and personable, but something was missing.

"There's little public interest in the Moon," Schmitt said. "Kids aren't as excited about it as we thought they'd be." He blamed the news media. It wasn't clear what the media were supposed to do.

Finally a woman in the audience asked a question about the Moon and his experiences. His response centered around the cliches of weightlessness and problems of eating. More questions followed on energy. Then the meeting was ended.

I sat stunned, wondering if I'd read the article by Goodavage .correctly. I dashed up to the head table before Sehmitt could get away.

"The Russians and some others have skid that anomalies were seen by astronauts on the Moon," I said. "Anomalies which might suggest intelligence. Or at least sights that were out of the ordinary. Did you see anything like that?" He smiled pleasantly, and his answer was smooth.

"Not at all. And our resolution was, of course, very good. Far better than the pictures."

"Not a thing," I repeated in disbelief. "Nothing extraordinary such as—"

"Nothing," he said. Then his voice was like that of an announcer or automaton, saying things in which he was completely disinterested. "Of course, I am perfectly willing to believe in the possibility of life in the universe. Out of many billions of stars . . ."

"Thanks," I said, and retreated. There were too many Air Force officers and Harvard old boys waiting for cabs in front of the building, so I walked. Half an hour later, I was no nearer my office. But I was, I thought, nearer the truth.

The military and intelligence-agency minds—how they think. Something perhaps like this: there are alien beings on the Moon. They do not relate or talk to us (although sometimes They say conflicting and confusing things to humans who do not have any official status, thereby creating myths and rumors which require special attention to dispel). This means They could be unfriendly. Potentially unfriendly aliens constitute a security threat to the country. Any security threat must be met by definite and effective steps. The first of these is to throw a security blanket over the subject.

Were the key scientists and astronauts under a security blanket? Did that explain Harrison Schmitt's speech and a host of other things? Hadn't Dr. Wittcomb said that the Moon program was first and foremost a military-engineering operation? From my experience with the data, I had become convinced that an official who categorically stated that the Moon was not occupied with an alien intelligence had to be one of the following:

(a) unfamiliar with the data (some people really do talk out of ignorance).

(b) untruthful (whatever the reason, including security).

(c) incompetent.

But you know and I know that (c) is not broadly true for officials discussing the Moon; there are incisive intelligences and brilliant minds working in and with NASA. And (a) is untrue in most cases; my knowledge of the data, after years of poring over pictures, is probably slight compared to that of the scientists and analysts who command the research output of others. The biggest revelation to me was that this argument was also proof—in addition to the changes on the Moon and the repairs and the long-lasting lights—that They were there now, this year, today, and we were looking not just at relics but at present construction. And some top policy-makers in our Government had to be awfully scared, judging by the tip of the iceberg visible to me.

And, ashing myself when does security end, 1 thought of the man who wrote of falls from the sky of blood and ice, of a thousand and more things ignored or damned by science—Charles Fort—who said, "I conceive of nothing, in religion, science or philosophy, that is more than the proper thing to wear, for a while."

CHAPTER THIRTEEN
If They Aren't Dust Clouds and Mists -- What Are They?

I had long been concerned with the puffs of dust, the mists, the clouds on the Moon: whitish puffs of something which hovered above the ground and were sometimes transparent. Some of them looked like our clouds on Earth when seen from above in a jet. They sometimes obscured a particular crater, and other times they spread out over a larger area. There were also the hazy conglomerations that looked like mists. They moved over crater floors, making the features appear blurred.

I knew about the gas ejections, of course. These gases behaved differently: they distorted the landscape slightly, they were blown out of discreet nozzles. They did not obscure completely, nor did they hover above the ground.

What was the cause of the clouds and mists?

Astronomers for many years have been seeing these phenomena, and have attributed them to various natural events: ice trapped in crevices turning to vapor in burning midday heat; volcanic eruptions; pulverization effect of meteorites; gases trapped under the surface of the Moon and escaping; and other natural causes, including tricks that solar flares play on the eye.

It was time to learn what the physical properties of the clouds and mists were, to think, and to develop new theses uninhibited by the current orthodoxies of astronomy. My experience so far had been that if an orthodox explanation for a phenomenon sounded foolish (as many did), it had probably been cooked up to avoid the occupancy thesis and was wrong. How could clouds and mists behave in the

vacuum of the Moon? What kinds of clouds and mists could be considered possible there? What was the latest thinking by physicists?

In past efforts I had been accused of being disorderly. Sam Wittcomb once challenged me with visions of change on the Moon; he'd said I acted like a whore on the Alaska pipeline.

"Just because you're not trained as a scientist does not mean you shouldn't work in a systematic way. It's easy to do sloppy work when you're not pushed. There's data in the pictures you haven't even come close to yet. I'd rather you found it yourself. Dig in."

"But I've already dug—"

"You've found a lot of interesting stuff," Sam agreed. "But imagine there are five hundred people after the same data. What then?"

I'd admitted I would work harder, more systematically.

With this wrist-slapping hanging over me, I headed north one morning on Route 270 (the highway Eisenhower built so he could get more easily to his farm in Gettysburg), up past the new technical plants and the thousands of town houses spawned by them, to the National Bureau of Standards.

My physicist friend with whom I had an appointment was one of the better scientists in an agency known for its quality of professional staff. He leaned his head back against a scientific apparatus I did not recognize and said, "Let's take the clouds first. Clouds of gas. They're billions of atoms with no binding between them. They're bounding around, hitting each other like crazy. Get the picture?"

"I get it."

"So this gas wants to disperse, to expand. It has to expand, if there's room at all. Put some gas in a closed room and it'll expand to fill the room. Put it in a vacuum and it shoots out in all directions."

"Then on the Moon ..."

"We'll come to that. It's a good definition of 'futility'—a gas expanding to fill the .vacuum on the Moon. Now. Keep in mind that a gas must have either an internal energy or energy from an external source. The sun in the middle of the day on the Moon would be an energy source. Heat deep inside the Moon, such as the cause of a volcano, would be another. Take away all the energy from a gas, inside and outside, and it'll become inert, a solid or a liquid. It wouldn't be a gas anymore."

He looked at me as though he had this great punch line to deliver.

"Only trouble is," the physicist said, "what would hold a cloud of gas together on the Moon?"

We both pondered that for a moment.

"I can see gas escaping from a fissure," he said. "I can see a trapped liquid turning into gas as the Moonscape heats up during the day. I can see a gas coming from any number of natural causes. I just can't see what would hold it together in a cloud. It'd be long gone."

I took notes. "So clouds of gas on the Moon are out Except for a fleeting moment. Let's move on to mists."

The physicist looked thoughtful, as though he wanted to add some reservations to my hasty dismissal of the subject. He leaned over to his in-box on the lab counter, fingered some publications, scratched his name off the route slip on a couple, then tossed them into his out-box.

"A mist consists of lots of tiny droplets. The atoms are bound, unlike the atoms of a gas. But they are not rigid like a solid. They're more subject to gravity than gas particles. In a vacuum, what's to keep mist particles up? I mean, that's what a mist is, isn't it—a lot of tiny droplets kept suspended above the ground? If they're on the ground, then it's not a mist anymore. It's moisture on the ground, dew, wetness."

I shrugged. What, indeed, would keep a mist up above the ground in the vacuum of the Moon?

"I doubt very seriously that water droplets on the Moon would stay together long enough to be detachable," the physicist said. He sounded quite certain. "A mist couldn't even exist in the first place. Not unless it were sprayed out, but then it would fall, or disperse and disappear fast."

"I take it you wouldn't catch a self-respecting mist on the Moon just hovering around," I said. I hated what I was hearing. It meant my job was harder. It meant we were seeing things on the Moon which were not as they appeared. They could not be labeled. They did not even exist, according to known laws.

"Not by a damn sight," the physicist said.

We talked for a couple of minutes about how the Bureau had grown in seventy-odd years from a room where they

kept the standards for weights and length (keeping them from moisture and changing temperature) to a vast complex employing three thousand people.

"That leaves only dust clouds," I said when the time seemed right.

He looked at me as though I'd asked him to make a speech in Philadelphia.

"They're impossible," he said.

When he saw my expression, he said quickly, "You can't have dust clouds without gaseous action, without air in and around the cloud, without wind to stir up the dust. Something's got to make the cloud in the first place. It can't make itself. Ever looked at dust particles in a shaft of sunlight? Watched the particles bounce around? That's called Brownian motion. Impossible on the Moon. Impossible to have a billowing cloud of dust."

I looked at my notes, but they were a blur. Flashes of scenes scudded across my eyeballs. I saw pictures with dust high above the ground. Billowing dust clouds on the sides of ravines, on crater rims, on cliffs.. NASA bigwigs might say they were optical illusions caused by the scattering of light. Orthodox astronomers might say the picture was snapped at the precise moment that a meteorite hit. And now this heavyweight physicist was telling me they just didn't exist.

"But say you're standing on the Moon," I persisted.

"Okay. I'm standing on the Moon."

"You kick the dirt under your feet. What—"

"Oh, right," the physicist said. "Dust will get raised, naturally. But it'll fall right back again. It won't hang around in a cloud."

There was an odd look on his face. I waited.

"And don't forget," he said. "I'm not there kicking up the dirt."

I had to agree with that. But who was?

"Suppose you hit the side of a cliff on the Moon," I said. "Hit it hard. And the cliff is composed of rock chips embedded in a fine soil. Won't the dust fly out from the cliff and billow a little from the light gravity as it falls down?"

"Sure," he conceded. "As long as there's someone there to hit the cliff."

"And if you use sort of a snow blower in the sandy dirt on the Moon, you know? Something that sucks up the dirt

and blows it out? Then I suppose you'll get a spray of dust."

He nodded. "A spray of dust, or a spray of anything, for that matter, will shoot up and out a lot farther on the Moon than on the Earth. Much lower gravity."

In my enthusiasm for what I believed to be a confirmatory point, I pursued this theme. We discussed the action of dust in a vacuum for another fifteen minutes, but the basic facts had already been established:

(1) It is virtually impossible to have a hovering cloud, mist, dust, or gas on the Moon.

(2) All of these entities might be seen for a limited time as they were being ejected from a container or stirred up.

(3) Gases, steam, and mist would all disperse very quickly in the vacuum of the Moon's environs.

(4) Dust could clearly be seen if it were raised or knocked down from a cliff, but it would settle soon.

(5) The chances are that the dust seen in the Moon craters where X-drones were working was being continually raised, as opposed to the slight chance that the picture was taken just at the right moment when a rare dust cloud had just been raised, as by a meteorite.

I prepared to leave. We'd already shaken hands when the physicist said something which endeared him to me. Suddenly he was more than a spewer of textbook facts. He said something which even I had forgotten about in my own zeal to get the facts. He could have written the first chapter of this book.

"One cautionary word." I stopped. "Our conversation is based on our knowledge to date. The so-called terrestrial limit. Man's limit. God knows if we'll have to readjust our knowledge out there."

I swear there was not even a twinkle in his eye as he said it.

Three good examples of these phenomena were fresh in my mind: billowing clouds (but they couldn't be) along the Apennine Mountains; mist (but it couldn't be) hovering over the crater near where Ranger Seven impacted; and dust (but it couldn't be) on the sides of King Crater, where the X-drones were working.

I spent the next three days in the library, searching

for a history of clouds, mists, and dust on the Moon. It was a fantastic history, one the average person probably doesn't dream exists. One you won't even get in a course in astronomy. Some of the highlights (only a few—the examples number in the thousands) went like this:

• P. Moore: "Obscurations have been reported [in Messier] from time to time, and on one occasion Klein described Messier as being 'filled with mist, from 1880 to date.' "

• Dinsmore Alter reported a veiling of the floor in Alphonsus in 1956.

• P. Moore: "Alter suggested that the cause [of the veiling in Alphonsus] was a slight discharge of gas from the tiny, very black spots lying along the clefts, forming a local and possibly short-lived atmosphere. ... He added that on two occasions the same sort of thing had been recorded in Linne."

• Fred Whipple: "A number of observers have noted haziness, brightening, or reddish coloration in certain crater floors and around the edges of certain craters and maria," from the late 18th century to the present.

• Whipple: "On November 3, 1958, N. A. Kozyref at the Kharkov Observatory was guiding the slit of his spectrograph on the central peak of crater Alphonsus. He first observed that the peak 'Became strongly washed out and of an unusual reddish hue.' Two hours later he 'was struck by its unusual brightness and whiteness at the time.' ... It appears that gas effusion from the crater lasted for not less than half an hour and not more than two and one-half hours that night. These and other observations indicate strongly that on rare occasions appreciable quantities of gases are emitted from cracks or craters in the lunar surface. Possibly there are occasional 'morning fog' effects in certain of the craters."

• Whipple: "B. M. Middlehurst and P. A. Moore have catalogued some 400 similar reports, including one nearly two centuries old by William Herschel."

• F. H. Thornton in 1949 saw a patch of "thin smoke or vapor" in the Herodotus Valley, which spread over the edge onto an adjoining plain. The smoke or cloud or vapor blurred the Moonscape.

• Obscurations in the crater Plato have been so numerous that it is the single favorite feature of amateur astronomers. They have been reported for over a hundred years.

• Schickard has been reported filled with "whitish mist," prior to 1900 and well into the 20th century.

• E. E. Barnard saw a pale luminous haze in Thales, early in this century.

• Charbonneaux, the French astronomer, saw an unmistakable white cloud form in the Apennine Mountains.

• Picard Crater in Mare Crisium has been obscured many times since late in the 19th century.

• W. H. Pickering, who first predicted the existence of Pluto in 1919, thought he saw hoarfrost in Messier and the crater named after him, as well as cloud-like features along the Apennines, and what looked like vapor coming from craterlets near Herodotus.

• T. A. Cragg observed an "obscuring matter" slowly covering the floor of Plato.

• Flammarion Book of Astronomy: "The Moon's surface is dusty. How was the dust formed, and where did it come from? . . . Meteoric dust would certainly not distribute itself in this way ... It must be assumed that the dusty material arises mainly from the disintegration of surface rocks *in situ* ... On the time scale of human geology, the erosion process is very rapid, every new formation being quickly covered with a dusty blanket. The existence of the latter can be verified even on the steepest slopes, such as that of the almost vertical Straight Wall. It sticks on by electrostatic or photoelectric effects, combined with the ; Moon's feeble gravity."

• Moore: "Three times in 1948 I saw the whole area [Graham Crater] 'misty gray and devoid of detail,' with the surrounding surface sharp and clearcut."

• C. Sagan in modern times writes that, tens of meters below the surface of the Moon, there might be a layer of organic material. (Gases or mists could conceivably emanate from this layer. Bear in mind that organic matter implies life.)

• A. Deutsch, a Russian astronomer, suggested in 1961 that, in view of the constant temperature below the outer coating of the Moon, gases might exist there to support plant or animal life.

• Moore: "Either we are dealing with gaseous emission from the Moon's crust, forming what may be termed a temporary and localized atmosphere either'of gas or dust, or else all the observations are wrong."

• Obscurations have been repeatedly found in the Hyginus Rille area for ninety years or more.

• Moore: "Let us repeat that the few professionals who have carried out really serious lunar observing have joined the amateurs in confirming the existence of obscurations."

• Wilkins and Moore: "Some observers have suggested that gases of unknown composition are occasionally ejected from cracks or sub-lunarian cavities beneath the surface. . . . Selenography must be founded on observation, not on preconceived and often erroneous conceptions." (Italics added.)

On and on. This is hard data written by scientific men of stature: men from all over the world, heavyweights such as Whipple and Moore. Wilkins and Sagan. I could, on this subject alone, fill volumes. Clouds and mists and obscurations must, according to the record, be as natural to the Moon as the craters which pock its surface.

Yet continuous clouds and mists and gases cannot be. The modem physicists say so. They would immediately disperse, not hang together long enough to obscure a crater floor for minutes or hours. One would not find a cloud of gas staying together in a puffy white state long enough to move around or even long enough to be photographed by Orbiter or Apollo cameras.

Were the clouds and mists controlled in some way? Were they really small particles under control of the Moon's occupants? I reminded myself of my own dictum: the Moon is a whole new ball game, we have to change our ways of thinking, get out of the mental straitjacket. We must realize that some phenomena might be beyond our comprehension. Life itself could take the form of clouds or mists under control. There could even be intelligence in the form of pure energy. There is no limit in theory to the form which intelligence could take.

But somehow I could not bring myself to believe that the j explanation was that far out or complex. 1 was intrigued J by the idea of clouds composed of particulates which, when j stirred up, remained in the form of a cloud for perhaps a i! couple of minutes because of the light gravity on the Moon j; and the lightness of the particles. (I could conceive of j enormous flying objects with rotating rings, stirring up the ;| dust for a mile or two around.) There had to be an answer i which reconciled the thousands of observations of clouds and mists with the basic laws of physics—even physics on the Moon.

And Wilkins and Moore, that team which carried the burden of the Moon for the professional astronomers hack when the Moon was a drag, said in their book, The Moon (Faber and Faber, 1960): "It is not impossible that on the Moon there may exist, or have once existed, some form of life peculiar to the Moon and totally unlike anything ever known on Earth."

CHAPTER FOURTEEN
Lights and Flashes and Flares: Let There Be Light— For Life

"Hey!" shouted Harrison H. Schmitt, Lunar Module Pilot" for the Apollo 17 space vehicle. It was during the first revolution around the Moon on that mission. "I just saw a flash on the lunar surface! It was just out there north of Grimaldi. You might see if you got anything on your seismometers, although a small impact probably would give a fair amount of visible light. It was a bright little flash near the crater at the north edge of Grimaldi; the fairly sharp one to the north [small crater north of Grimaldi B] is where there was just a thin streak of light."

It was the same area where the Command Module Pilot during the Apollo 16 flight also reported seeing a "flash of bright light."

The next day, during the fourteenth revolution around the Moon, the Command Module Pilot for Apollo 17 Ronald E. Evans, also reported seeing a flash near the rim of Mare Orientale. His comments, as taped during the flight, were "Hey! You know, you will never believe it. I am right over the edge of Orientale. I just looked down and saw a light flash myself. Right at the end of the rille that is on the east of Orientale."

NASA publicly attributes many of the flashes seen on the Moon to meteorites striking. Others are blamed on cosmic rays going through the eye. One interesting facet of the transcripts quoted above, however, along with the report from Apollo 16, is this: two meteorites have almost no chance of striking the identical spot on successive days. The odds against it happening are prohibitive. And the cosmic- ray hypothesis does not hold water for these particular sighting either: cosmic rays cause generalized flashes, cannot be pinpointed as to an exact location within a crater, and move laterally across the eyeball as opposed to flashing. But it is easier to reach out for any explanation than to create waves in the pond of orthodoxy.

Dr. Farouk El-Baz helped train the astronauts. I am indebted to Joseph Goodavage for the report of the following statement (referred to earlier) made by Dr. El-Baz when he was questioned about the many anomalies associated with Moon lights which could not be explained naturally:

"The one thing I can't explain—that I do not know about or what it could be—are these enormous flashes of light. There's no question about it, they are very tremendous things: not comets, not natural. Three were seen over the western part of the Moon,"one*by Ken Mattingly on Apollo 16 and two by Ron Evans and Jack Schmitt on Apollo 17."

There. "Not natural." "Enormous flashes of light." No person knew more about the physics and geology of the Moon than Dr. El-Baz, and he was certainly familiar with the Cosmic Ray Light Flash Phenomenon. If they are not natural or mistaken perception by the astronauts, then they must be associated with the intelligent occupants of the .Moon.

The light flashes resulting from cosmic rays occurred even while the men were blindfolded during a test on the Apollo 17 mission. The flashes were described as almost instantaneous and could never be associated with real flashes on the ground.

On several other occasions the astronauts saw bright lights in craters. Once a light was seen rising slowly up from the dark Moon horizon. On Apollo 16 Ken Mattingly said, "Another strange sight over here. It looks—a flashing light—think it's Annbell." ("Annbell" was, of course, a code word of something to be on the lookout for, and probably meant something like "manufactured construction" i or "moving object." Another code word was "Barbara.") Meteorites do not create flashing lights, nor has the Light | Flash Phenomenon from cosmic rays ever confused the I highly trained astronauts.

Astronomers have reported strange bright lights in the craters Aristarchus and Plato, among hundreds of others.

Ruby-red color flashes have been seen repeatedly in Aristarchus. They cover areas up to several miles long and are often seen over domelike structures. The Russians have documented luminescent glow in Aristarchus. Spectrographic analysis of these glows showed emission lines similar to those of molecular hydrogen gas. These flashes and glows are not generally seen when the sun hits the central peaks—that is, they cannot be attributed to the sun, otherwise they would be a common phenomenon at that time of day.

Moore says that "flashes on the Moon are very rare indeed. However, some have been recorded, notably by the ALPO (Association of Lunar and Planetary Observers) observers and by Tsuneo Saheki in Japan, who, on 25th August 1950, saw what he termed a stationary yellowish- white flare lasting for quarter of a second."

Rare? Thousands of reports of flashes, glows, and flares add up to "rare"?

F. H. Thorton, in 1948, saw a brilliant flash of light at the western rim of Plato. He likened it to the flash of an antiaircraft shell exploding in the air ten miles away.

M.K. Jessup, a mathematician-astronomer who was one of the first serious writers to link the Moon with UFOs, reported from his research that specks of light lasting an hour or more were seen all during the nineteenth century.

Lights are rare on the Moon?

Volcanism is also blamed for lights. I quote from the Apollo Preliminary Science Report, NASA SP-330, 1973: "With the conclusion of Apollo 17, it has been suggested that volcanic activity in the highland region subsequent to approximately 3 billion years ago may be highly restricted or virtually non-existent. Apollo experiments investigating whether the Moon is 'alive' or 'dead' indicate that, compared with Earth, the Moon is seismically quiet ... A quiet Moon is consistent with the conclusion that volcanism and other types of tectonic activity have been rare or absent from the lunar surface for the last 2 to 3 billion years . . . From the Apollo program, we can conclude that the Moon, at one time, was very much alive and now is very quiet."

So lights on the Moon are not thought to be caused by volcanic action. (Keep in mind the conundrum posed by the NASA statement: if the Moon is so quiet, how then can we account for the high seismic readings in the Bullialdus-Lubinicky area?) And meteoric impacts cannot account, for lights lasting minutes or an hour. And the sun, hitting mountain peaks at dawn cannot account for lights, in an area where the sun is not due to shine for days. And there is no spontaneous combustion of escaping gases, because fireTcToes not burn without available oxygen.

When we see lights on the Moon coming from the same places in craters, when we see flares lasting minutes and hours, we are looking at light created by the occupants of the Moon. These lights are the logical result of their activity in constructing things, mining, repairing, moving about, and perhaps—just once in a while—enjoying themselves.

Herschel, that musician-turned-astronomer who discovered the planet Uranus, saw during a total eclipse about 150 very bright spots scattered over the surface of the Moon.

Dozens of observers have reported seeing glimmering blue lights.

"Specklings" of lights are common. These clusters sometimes look like bright needle points huddling together. The record shows that white dots of lights in an arc have been seen often, particularly in the Mare Crisium.

In 1821 a light shone out with startling brightness from the crater Aristarchus—for two days in February. Then it was seen again by others. Then twice in May the same sharp light shone from the same crater.

Gruithuisen back in 1824 watched a light in one location flash intermittently for a full half-hour.

Charles Fort wrote about signal-like lights seen on the Moon. He took his data from scientific journals. Minute dots and streaks of light in Mare Crisium: the phenomena recurred over and over, 120 years of lights in Mare Crisium. And he told of designs in lights—two straight lines of lights, with a dark band between them which was covered with luminous points. This configuration, obviously of intelligent design, was sighted by Gruithuisen in Messier.

Hodgson saw a bright light on December 11, 1847. The light flashed intermittently. Charles Fort liked to fancy They were signaling. (I think that is nonsense, that the occupants of the Moon don't give a damn about us, to say nothing about signaling to us.)

The years 1864-1865 were great for Picard, in the Mare Crisium. It is a smallish crater you can easily miss if conditions are not good for viewing. But a man named Herbert Ingall watched a small point of light there "glitter like a star." It was seen by others over long periods of time; then it was gone—replaced by a cloud.

For those who observed with any regularity during

the first half of the nineteenth century, the Moon was a prime performer. It glittered and sparkled and flared and flashed. | These years since the turn of the century have been fascinating, and NASA's efforts—pictures and landings—have made them astounding. The lights continue.

Birt and Eiger saw such an extraordinary arrangement of lights in Plato that they combined with other Moon observers to study and chart them. The lights were fixed in location—but rose and fell in intensity. Fort reports that up to April, 1871, the selenographers had recorded 1600 observations on the fluctuations of Plato's lights. These, with graphs and complete records, were deposited in the Library of the Royal Astronomical Society. Could anyone possibly say lights on the Moon are rare?

The *Astronomical Register* reported that a Prague astronomer saw, on April 24, 1874, a dazzling white object. slowly crossing the surface of the Moon. *He continued to watch it after it left the Moon.* Thirteen years later, a luminous triangle was watched on the floor of Plato. In the same year several observers watched "flakes" of light moving toward Plato from all the other craters of the Moon,. This year, some readers may know, was in The so-called incredible decade on Earth—incredible because of the unidentified objects which flew everywhere, incredible because the two moons of Mars were discovered for the first time officially (they'd been written about before in fiction!) by Dr. Asaph Hall, incredible because an airship hysteria rampaged across the country as "something" was tracked from coast to coast and back to Chicago.

And Plato—normally a dark, brooding walled plain near the northern edge of the Moon—blazed with lights.

I like to think of Plato as convention headquarters for the occupants of the Moon. "A blizzard of shining points gathering into light-drifts in Plato." wrote Charles Fort in New Lands. "Then the denizens of Aristarchus and of Kepler, and dwellers from the lunar Alps, each raising his torch, marching on a triangular path, making the triangle shine in the dark."

But lights on the Moon do not fit in with the current lunar theory: that volcanism is practically nonexistent, that a meteorite flash cannot last for a minute, that a meteorite flash also cannot move around and change colors. So "lights on the Moon are rare."

Rarer still are the astronomers who communicate in com- mon-sense terms the really important things happening to this Earth and Moon.

The Lunar-Transient-Phenomena Study

NASA began studying "transient phenomena" on the Moon during the 1960s in earnest. LTP of interest included anything showing movement, color, light, obscuration— anything different from the usual.

In the June, 1972, issue of Strolling Astronomer, NASA announced a formal program for observing Lunar Transient Phenomena. An urgent appeal was made for observers— those with appropriate-sized telescopes and sufficient experience to understand the main objectives and operating methods. Thirty-two observers responded. Each observer was assigned four sites which had repeatedly shown LTP in the past, one non-LTP site for comparison, and one of the zones from which positive seismic (Moonquake?) reports had been received. Only six observers reported with any regularity, and then not always on the features assigned to them. One conclusion to draw from this is that astronomers, both professional and amateur, will do what they want to do when they want to do it.

Patrick Moore of England cataloged Lunar Transient Phenomena. An almost random sampling from his and W. S. Cameron's collection reveals that the following events have been happening for hundreds of years on the Moon and still go on:

Blinking, reddish colorations, starlike points, brightenings, pulsations, and blue lights, on the top of peaks and crater floor, have all been reported in Aristarchus.

Blinking, needle points, moving lights, and red color have been sighted in Plato.

Starlike points during eclipses have been sighted in a dozen or more craters.

Brightening, blinking on the outer wall and then on an

inner wall, a pinkish glow on the floor, and moving shadows on the wall have been seen in Gassendi.

Blinking on the inside wall, the appearance of fog cascading down the slope, and a cluster of spots of light have been reported in Eratosthenes.

Two spots blinked red for 28 minutes in Bjela^

A very bright blink in one small craterlet, a dim blink in another, and bright red flashes for fifteen seconds were sighted in Rabbi Levi.

The west rim was colored yellow ocher with a thin cloud in Posidonius.

An intermittent glow for two hours, brightening and obscuration of the inner.wall, a flash of first magnitude on the central peak, a reddish glow followed by obscuration, 'brightness lasting several minutes on the peak, flashing on top of the inside wall, a pinkish color to peaks and walls, an orange-pink glow on central mountains have all been reported in Theophilus.

Reddening in a fan formation, following a bright area, was seen south of Madler.

A pulsating White glow on the external west slope was sighted in Tycho.

The north wall was colored red and green, northwest

wall very brilliant, a brightening of the whole crater, an alternate brightening of the southern half at fifteen-second intervals, red color on the north-northwest wall for eighteen minutes were reported phenomena in Proclus.

And on and on. There are other lists. There are countless observations of strange events not reported. There are probably countless more which take place but axe never seen due to poor viewing conditions.

W. S. Cameron of NASA, who (along with Moore and Bartlett) has perhaps done more work in this field than anyone else, has a collection of well over 900 LTP dating back to the sixteenth century.

Some of Cameron's points in relation to these phenomena are as follows: *

[On starlike points:] The fact that they are starlike points rules out the Earth's atmosphere and indicates they are .5-2 sec. of arc in dimension which is equivalent to .5-2 miles at the Moon's surface. If they are glints it is puzzling that they are not seen at every lunation and that they were seen one night but not the next under similar, very good seeing conditions . . . Clearly this phenomenon needs explaining. It may be an instrumental effect, but there are several puzzling aspects concerning the matter.

[On obscurations:] Although the short-lived brightening's and starlike points might be considered to have explanations in instrumental, atmospheric, and geometric effects, there are other phenomena that seem to represent genuine, abnormal situations on the Moon. There are too many instances of obscuration or mists reported in which a portion of a crater or feature was fuzzy or blotted out while everything else around was very sharply visible. The fact that these are seen in only certain features . . . suggests that these are lunar phenomena and not terrestrial.

* W. S. Cameron, "Comparative Analyses of Observations of Lunar Transient Phenomena," Icarus 16, 339-387 (1972).

[On the origin of LTP:] From the analyses in the present paper, results from other lines of study and long and thoughtful consideration of the reports, it is concluded that the LTP are generally of internal origin and not much subject to external influences—at best only weakly so. The phenomena seem to be of several kinds and may involve gas or a gas-and-dust mixture, luminescence of these gases, and possibly luminescence of surface materials.

[On the nature of the gases:] A few events have been recorded spectrographically; the constituents or gases identified in 6 were C2, H2, and N2 which are common constituents in terrestrial volcanic gases. [These are gaseous forms of carbon, hydrogen and nitrogen.]

The internal activity must be mostly a gentle degassing—leaking of gas—and not volcanic on the terrestrial scale. If there were much of the latter, permanent changes would be expected to be observed, which is not the case. A few events seem to be of a magnitude that suggest volcanism, but most are not.

There have been many statistical correlations of the data, many LTP symposiums, many journal articles. Attempts have been made to explain LTP (particularly lights) on the basis of several theories.

One deals with the perimeters of dark maria, on the theory that the maria were made by huge lava flows, and that trapped gas under the lava flows seeps out around the edges.

Second, sunrise on the Moon—on the theory that the sun touches off certain light effects by ultraviolet excitation of gases escaped during the night.

The third theory is that Earth's magnetic tail accelerates solar particles which may reach local areas on the Moon.

The fourth concerns tidal effects. The theory is that

tides on the Moon are waterless but more significant than those of Earth. Thus, they can greatly affect the depth levels of gas trapped beneath the surface, particularly at eccentric apogees.

The fifth possibility is solar-flare particles, on the theory that they can create luminescent excitation.

The basis for the sixth theory is low-angle illumination, which renders any existing medium more visible than at high sun angles.

But W. S. Cameron doubts the validity of weak correlations with any of the hypotheses put forth to explain the Lunar Transient Phenomena. She indicates her belief that many different reasons exist for them. In other words, this group of lights in Plato may be caused by luminescence from solar flares, that glow in Aristarchus from volcanism, etc.

What are we to make of the data and work done to date? Let's take the reasons NASA and the scientists put forth to explain LTP one by one.

(1) Gas escapes from beneath large lava deposits which cover the dark maria. It escapes from around the edges.

(What accounts for the obscurations and lights in the middle of maria? On top of peaks? On the side of crater walls? How does gas show up as brilliant lights?)

(2) Sunrise on the Moon touches off light effects by ultraviolet excitation of gases.

(Why are so many lights seen not at sunrise?)

(3) The Earth's magnetic tail accelerates solar particles which reach local areas on the Moon.

(If this were true, the lights and glows and flashes would be general, random, and not confined to about ninety specific locations on the Moon.)

(4) Tidal effects on the Moon tend to cause gases to escape at eccentric apogees.

(So gases escape. Escaping gases do not normally have various colors, various patterns, various rhythms.)

(5) Solar-flare particles create luminescent excitation. (As in [3] above, why are they confined to special areas? If escaping gases in special areas are "excited," why do they blink in rhythm and in different colors? Why are there bright points of light equivalent to patches up to two miles in diameter? Can brilliant flares of light be compared with simple luminescence?)

(6) Low-angle illumination makes existing media more visible than at high sun angles.

(This hypothesis makes no sense at all in explaining the wide variety of LTP. Yes, a ridge on the Moon becomes more visible at low-angle illumination. But low-angle illumination does not create patterns of lights, flares, blinking, obscurations, etc.)

(7) Volcanic action causes belching fire, which causes the lights and smoke, which causes the obscurations.

(NASA admits that the Moon is relatively dead so far as current volcanism is concerned. And eruptions of that size would result in definite changes and other observable evidence.)

(8) Meteorites striking rock and breccia create flashes. (But not long-lasting flares, patterns of lights at the same time, different colors, obscurations, etc.)

The scientists go on reaching out, striving desperately to find a "natural" cause for LTP, finally arriving at the point where they settle for "If one of these hypotheses does not fit, then all or several in conjunction must be true." They avoid, consciously or unconsciously, the simple truth that occupants of the Moon cause Lunar Transient Phenomena as They go about Their very purposeful business.

And Loren Eiseley, the anthropologist whose writing makes your nervous system vibrate, touched a spider's web with a pencil and concluded that in the world of the spider he did not exist. Then he asked (The Unexpected Universe, Harcourt, Brace and World, 1969): "Is Man at heart any different from the spider? . . . man thoughts, as limited as spider thoughts .. . What is it we are a part of that we do not see, as the spider was not gifted to discern my face, or my little probe into her world?"

CHAPTER FIFTEEN
Markings, Insignia, and High-rise Signals

The soldier, bleary-eyed after beering it up in town, gazed unsteadily at the sea of barracks: endless barracks. all the same, in all directions. All were painted the same drab color and all were the same distance apart and all had the same lights burning in front and back. Even the GI streets in between looked alike.

He fought to keep his eye open and looked around. On the comer was a sign, pointing to the left: 11th AKMD INF DXV, 21st INF BN, co c. He brightened. Thank God for insignia. He tottered off in that direction, knowing he'd be in his bunk in a few minutes.

The occupant of the space vehicle maneuvered the disc up slowly from the isolated Canadian lake, slipped rapidly sideways in the direction of the Moon on the horizon, and a few hours later was skimming Mare Imbrium. Thousands of craters, as far as the eye (!) could see. Craters the size of dimples, craters miles in diameter. Craters with the same tan-gray color, same rims white in the sun. The occupant of the space vehicle circled, came lower. On the lip of the crater- below was the legend:

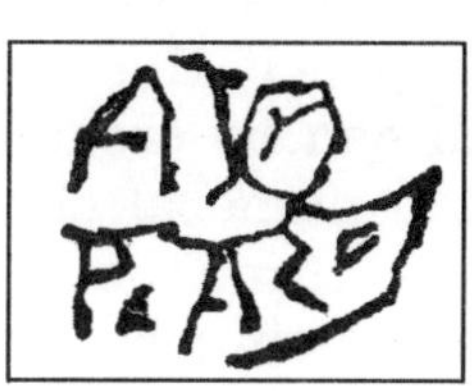

He made sounds of satisfaction. His clan, his group.

In four minutes he'd be unloading the big tank full of fresh water. Four minutes to a comfortable atmosphere, air he could breathe, temperature he liked. He was tired of the water run to Earth, and it was good to see the insignia beside the crater.

That "insignia" is found in the last Ranger Seven picture, taken with the F-a camera 3.7 miles above the Moon's surface, less than three seconds before impact. The insignia fascinates me because of the repetition of what looks like our letter A and the regularity of the other characters.

The Moon's surface is covered with markings of similar interest. There is no weather—no rain or wind—to erode them. The only possible eroding factors are (a) erasure by intelligent movement either on purpose or by accident; (b) erasure over eons by the slow relentless fall of space and Moon dust; (c) volcanic action. Otherwise, a marking on' the Moon stays as it is. The result is that one cannot examine the ground in a closeup picture carefully without seeing many markings of interest.

Below is another glyph of which I am particularly fond. It is also located in a final Ranger picture. The temptation is to read all sorts of things into it. For example, I like to see alpha and omega, but this temptation should obviously be resisted. It is fun, too, to point out that the glyph has a beautiful repetitive theme; and where there is a blank below the line, a dotted line leads to it. And then there's the similarity of all the characters to ones we're familiar with! But it is worth repeating a point made in another chapter: there are only so many ways a line can be drawn; only so many turns of the pencil that can be made; only so many glyphs which can be created. I feel certain that all our alphabet and numeral characters are repeated on countless planets throughout our galaxy, without standing for the same things, the same concepts, the same sounds. (Except for rare coincidences!)

I do not know what this beautiful glyph means, but I am sure it means something to a clan of very intelligent beings.

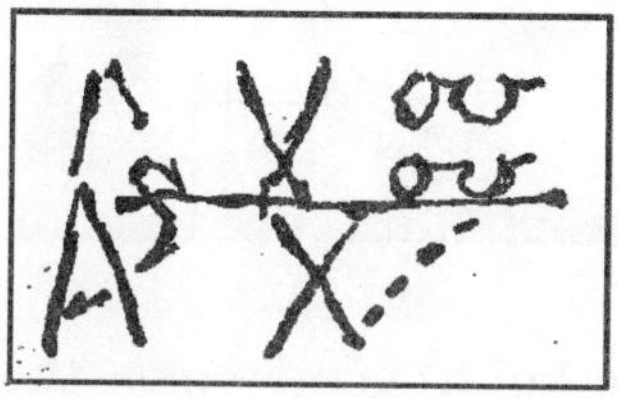

But, you say—if you are thinking at all—if the occupants i of the Moon use symbols, insignia, surely these markings would to some extent be repetitive. Surely some of them would be found in several places.

And they are. The glyphs which look like A's, Z's, and P's are found everywhere. We have already presented and considered the large perfect crosses gleaming on the lips of craters which are currently being sprayed out. I have found few craters being sprayed, or with ah X-drone on the bottom, which do not also have a giant cross on the lip.

You remember, of course, the wonderful glyph on the octagon in Tycho. The size of it means it can be seen from many miles up. And you have been introduced to the different shapes craters have. It is probable that each shape conveys a message. We can speculate that some of the messages might be "There is mining going on here," "This crater is now depleted of nickel," "This is the home of the Alpha Centauri clan," etc.

There are two kinds of "unfinished" craters. The one below is extremely common; I have seen only two examples of the one on the top of page 163.

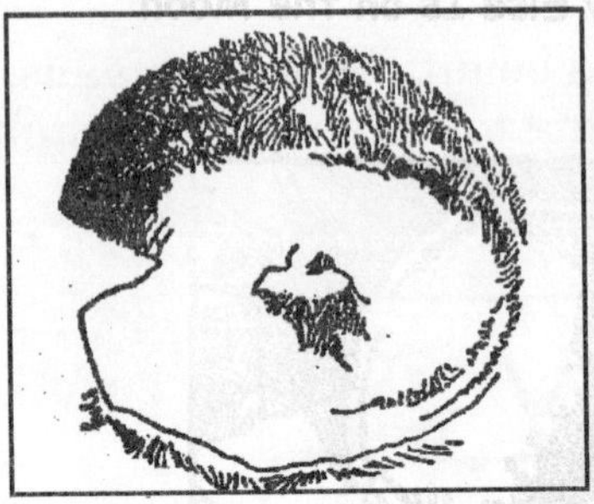

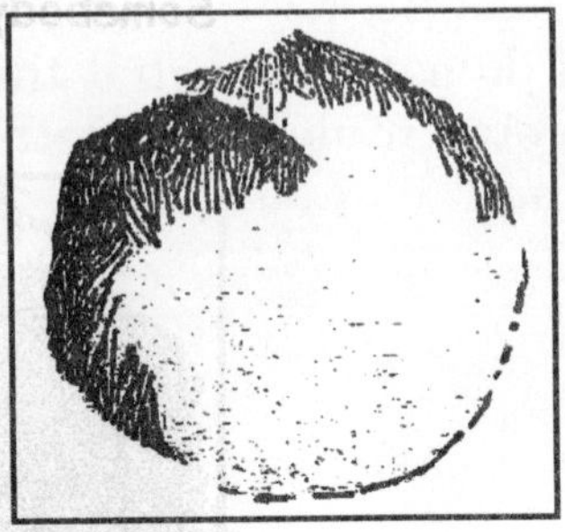

One could make a good case that the rim in the crater above does not represent a signal but simply is a convenient way to slice the rim, and I would not disagree. In fact, because the crater shape is unique, and because X-drones are working there, I would tend to weight this hypothesis over the other.

There is another phenomenon which we have not discussed yet. That is the "scraped ground" on the edge of certain smallish craters. The scraped ground is always in the form of a square or rectangle. In most cases the scraped areas are at ninety-degree intervals around the crater. Sometimes' there is only one. Two examples are sketched below and at the top of page 164.

Is this a signal? The only statement I can make with real confidence is that the scraped ground results from intelligent activity. Perhaps it represents spots where objects sat while spraying went on, and then the objects left, leaving the previously sheltered surface exposed.

Many craters have raised oblongs on their lips. Petavius and Lubinicky are good examples. The oblongs cast shadows. They slope downward from the raised rim to the ground. The lines of the oblongs are always perfectly straight.

There are mammoth E's and F's on the floors of some craters. A random E I can accept as being natural. But dozens of them? All as perfect as if drawn by an architect? Plato (on the left) and Gassendi (on the right) are outstanding examples:

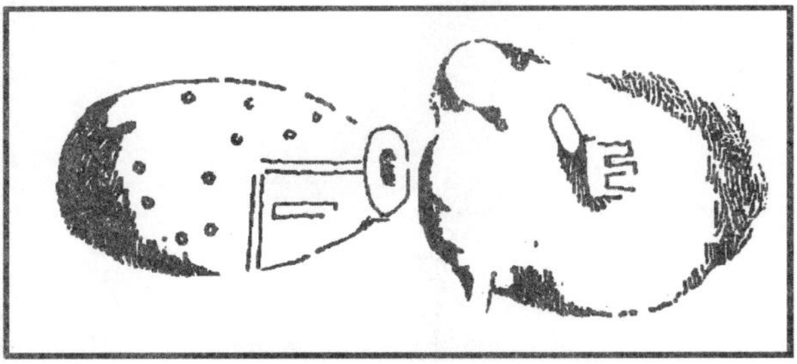

The floor of Copernicus is fascinating. The astronauts saw what has been referred to as construction in the central peaks. On the floor there is something which reminds one of the ancient architected monstrosities found on Earth which are relics of ancient times. It rises to a symmetrical peak, and on its side is a beautiful message!

For a time I kept a record of some of the more interesting glyphs and markings found on the Moon. The collection looks as though someone chose characters at random from all the alphabets of the earth, from shorthand drill books, from Chinese and hieroglyphic writings. One glyph turned out to look exactly like the following character sketch. It appealed to me because it is an old Hindi S joined to a Semitic S. Make something out of that at your own peril!

Too much attention to these glyphs and markings and signals leads to all sorts of fruitless conjecture. For example, I began to find letters similar to the old runic alphabet. If you did not know about runes before, you are in good company. It was a form of writing used in the northern countries of Europe in the third century A.D.

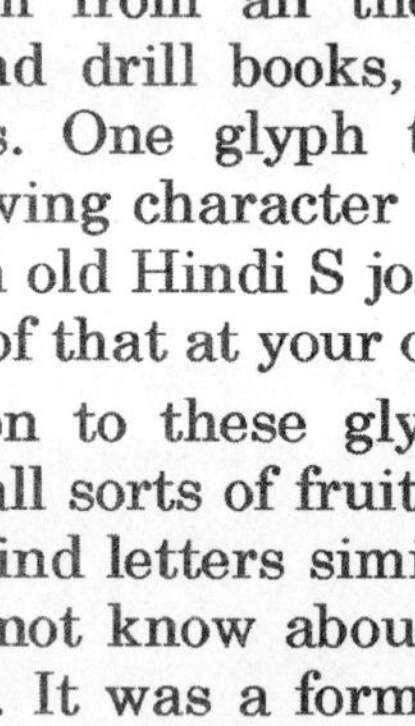

At times it was used all over Europe. Every rune-stave (letter) had a name. There were twenty-four of them. It is thought that runes originated with the Goths, those early plunderers of the dark ages, in southeastern Europe. Later the use of runes spread northward.

I was attracted to runes because I had seen the following rune-staves in markings on the Moon:

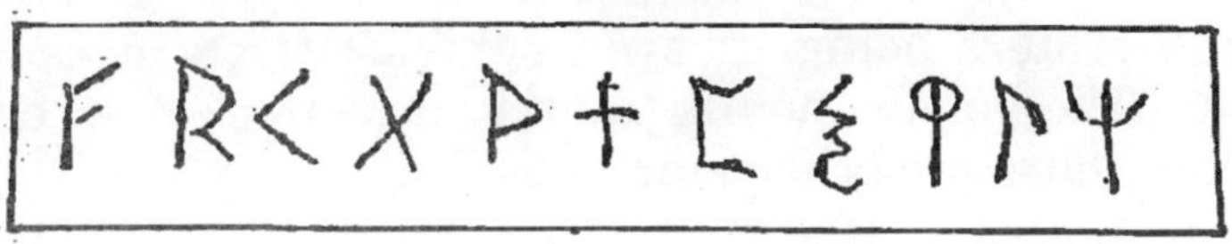

But there are many rune-staves I did not see on the Moon, and many other markings were sighted which bore no resemblance to them. In making analogies, one must be prepared to face examples which do not fit. One definite failure causes an entire theory to collapse. There are many examples of the glyph A on the Moon, but there is nothing like the A in the runic staves. Not a trace.

Another example of a marking which is repetitive over the Moon is the "tree of life" which we saw on the backs of the ovals in the crater near the Ranger Seven impact point. This glyph has been seen on the moon surface in many places, always encased in a circle or an oval. The tree of life is one of mankind's oldest symbols. Could it be possible that this and certain other symbols were copied from the occupants of the Moon during ancient confrontations on Earth? (For instance, notice the resemblance of this p;1vph to the, ancient Z of the Semites and Karosthians.)

There are directional signals on the Moon, too. The Simple arrow is seen pointing toward things of interest to the occupants. The best example is on the highlands near King Crater—that mysterious crater where so much change is shown. This is the area containing the small craters being sprayed out, discussed in Chapter Five. The arrow points in the direction of a hollow where there are other markings.

Markings on the Moon must be distinguished from raised objects and from those strange filaments making up the so-called grid system. These filaments are found every-

where, they cross craters at ground level, and sometimes they end at the crater lip with a tip jutting out. With filaments running at right angles to them, they often form a matrix or woven pattern. Some parts of the Moon's surface are so covered with these matrices that one is tempted to speculate that once the entire surface of the Moon was an artificial cover, that what we now see is the chaotic remains.

Signals Which Rise High in the Sky

There is a most interesting configuration on the Moon which takes the form of a thin tower rising for a mile or more. It is one of the clearest-cut indications of intelligence on the Moon. The towers are invariably straight and— most remarkably—when on a ridge or mountain mass, they always are placed at the highest point.

One form of this phenomenon was noticed by Russian lunar scientists and subsequently reported by Ivan

Sanderson. Most of these towers have received no notice. An exception has been the frank statement by Dr. Farouk El Baz, who told of enormous spires "*taller than the tallest building on Earth.*" He said they seemed to be constructed of material different from the surrounding Moonscape; and that none of the lunar landings came close enough to get surface pictures of the spires. They are whitish, El Baz said, with shadows stretching for many miles. We will classify them and other high-risers into basic types.

(a) *mountaintop "antennae"*: There are several mountain ranges and high crater rims where peaks have been carved into exotic shapes and their highest points topped with "towers" or interesting sculptures.

The "towers" gleam in the sunlight. Sometimes they rise at an angle, sometimes exactly vertically. NASA photos shot obliquely along valleys are the best way to see them. For an example of an unmistakable high-rise "tower," created by the occupants of the Moon, refer to the mountain mass on the right side of the central crater in plate 3.

Some are in the form of designs like simple Chinese characters. Three kinds of towers are sketched below.

(b) towers connected by a filament: For this example we return to the superb photographs of the Moon taken by Matsui at the Kwasan Observatory, Japan. Some are reproduced in Moore's A Survey of the Moon.

Plate No. 9"'in Moore's book shows Petavius. Between this crater and a crater to its right is an array of slanted poles, or towers, all rising at an agle of less than 45 degrees. A filament (possibly a cable?) can be seen running from tip to tip. My interpretation of this photo is below.

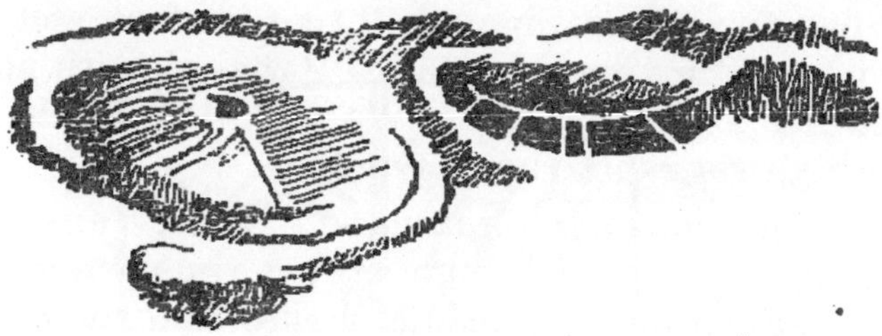

(c) *sentinels in the wasteland:* Many good examples exist of single towers rising straight up from the ground— not on peaks or highlands. In some cases there are towers spaced several miles apart and perfect aligned. My favorite is one which rises for perhaps a hundred feet or more and then turns suddenly horizontal at a perfect 90-degree angle. It is in plate 21 (67-H-187). It looks like this:

(b) *anomalous constructions:* variety' of strange high-risers delight and mystify. Beyond Pythagoras, beyond the Sea of Cold, one can find huge S-configurations, snaking their way skyward as though to pay a shaky homage to an unknown deity. Zigzag towers look smoky in the distance, perhaps from sun shining on mesh or metal filigree.

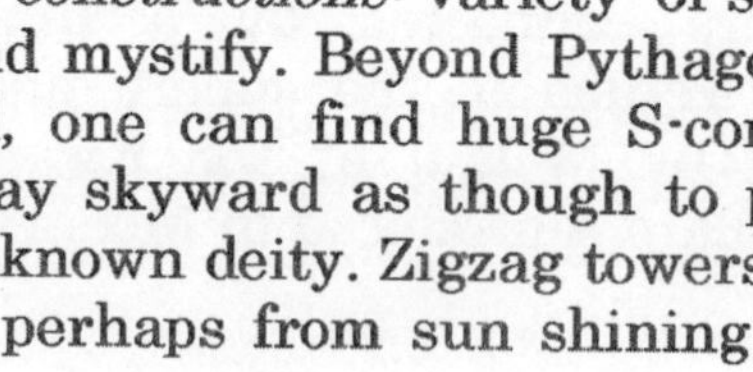

The size of these constructions varies from a few hundred yards to ten or more miles.

What is particularly interesting is their parallelism. We can say with virtually complete assurance that they represent the efforts of the occupants. The general characteristic of this curious feature is sketched below:

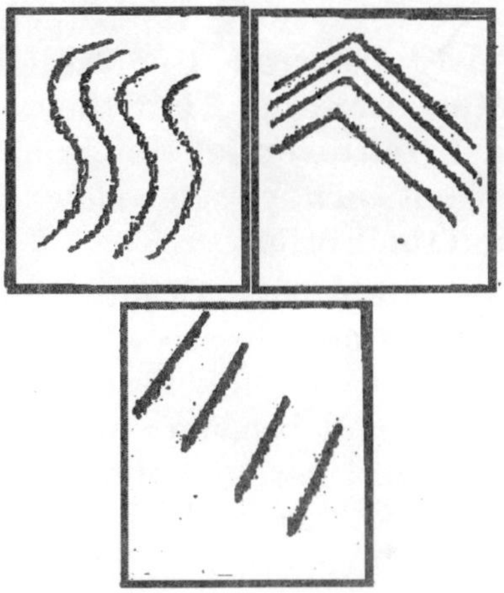

King Crater is as anomalous an area as exists on the J Moon. The theory of this book could stand alone on the evidence of features of that crater and environs. One of the many curious objects there is "something" which rises and curves like an ocean wave. It has a forked end. Its length must be approximately three miles. I have no idea what to make of it, and happily relegate it to the reservoir of natural phenomena—but this does not make it any the less mysterious. What kind of internal or other forces on the Moon could create it? Is there a' resemblance between this and some of the "high-risers" to be seen in Mare Crisium? At any rate, I have sketched this anomaly, in the hopes that someone1 will have an insight:

We previously referred (in the Preface) to the "bridges" of Mare Crisium. That they exist is probably one of the least controversial things about the Moon—now. It was not always so. Now the controversy revolves around their origin.

The entire area j)f Crisium is filled with constructions of various shapes which rise into the sky. Some are bent over, not touching the ground. Others touch the ground and become "bridges," (plate 1). To clarify my point, and perhaps show a similarity to the object sketched above, I will show how three of the Mare Crisium constructions or bent- over high-risers appear to me:

Beacons, Signals, and the Problem of Communications

A knowledge of basic physics helped me formulate a theory concerning the purpose of these phenomena. I was concerned about the proliferation of high-rise towers on the Moon, particularly the thin straight ones, which were not so aesthetically pleasing as were many of the others. What could they be used for? The answer is simple, and you probably have guessed it.

Radio and television waves travel readily through the Moon's near-vacuum. Our astronauts communicated by radio from space vehicle to lunar module on the ground, and from the Moon to ground control in Houston. Both radio and television waves are electromagnetic. These waves travel in a straight line.

Since the Moon is considerably smaller than Earth, the Moon's horizon is very close to an observer standing on the Moon. You can stand in a moderate-size crater, and the rim of that crater might well be beyond the horizon. It would be hard to imagine, in such a situation, that you were in a crater. The curvature of both Earth and the Moon presents a problem for radio and television waves. But the problems is more serious for the smaller Moon.

Too, the Moon has no Heaviside layer of ionized gas such as we have in our upper atmosphere. This layer can act as a mirror for radio waves of a certain long frequency.

It is easy to see that the occupants of the Moon could have a need to facilitate the transmission of electromagnetic waves. Towers to aid in transmitting these signals would be important. (A new dimension would be the receipt and transmission of electromagnetic radio waves between the Moon and Their home planets.) Some of the circular objects we see on the surface may be for the purpose of bringing in distant signals. Local and/or distant radio transmission is a feasible .explanation of many of the high-rise towers and other constructions on the Moon.

You are wondering why we do not pick up a constant gabble of Their communications on radio. One possibility is that Their rate of information transfer is so great that all we detect is noise. Indeed, if the transfer rate were sufficiently great, we might hear nothing at all. Another possibility is that we do pick up their communications but fail to recognize them as such.

The mathematics of radio- and television-wave coverage- over straight-line distances is easily worked out.

If d equals the distance an electromagnetic wave can travel to the horizon, r equals the radius of the Moon (1080), and h equals the height of the tower, then:

$r^2 + d^2 = (r + h)^2$ d

$d^2 = 2\,rh + h^2$

$d = \sqrt{2\,rh + h^3}$

But h^2 is insignificant relative to 2rh
(e.g., if h — 1 mile, then h^2 is 1/2160th of 2rh)

Therefore, d = approximately $\sqrt{2rh}$

And d = approximately 46.5 $\sqrt{h}$
If h = 1 mile, then d = 46.5 miles
If h = 4 miles, then d = approximately 93 miles (straight- line-distance the wave will travel) or a total area (using Pi r^2, or 3.14 x 93^2) of 27,158 square miles.

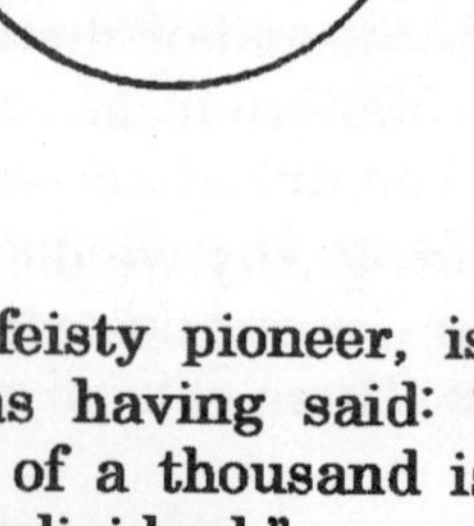

And Galileo, that feisty pioneer, is quoted in The New Mars (NASA) as having said: "In questions of science the authority of a thousand is not worth, the reasoning of a single individual."

CHAPTER SIXTEEN
Assorted Oddities

Some phenomena resist classification because of their strangeness. Dipping down into that bag with no particular priority, we come up with these:

Giant Ladder—or Tread from Mammoth Vehicle

Plate 22 (69-H-8) is an oblique view from the Apollo 8 spacecraft of a large area on the lunar far side. In it is an almost obliterated crater with many parallel markings running through it. One set of these parallel markings continues in the air from the rim of the crater on into its bottom. It appears to be an enormous rope ladder or, conceivably, the tread from a very large vehicle. NASA does not identify the size of the crater or give a good bench mark for judging the distance, but my guess is that the "rope ladder" is about four miles long.

Here is my impression of it. (Page 175)

The object seems to cast a shadow on the floor of the crater. If this is a shadow, then the phenomenon is not a tread but more analogous to a leaning ladder. The phenomenon is very real but it almost—and this is typical of so many Moon oddities—defies description. This is perhaps because we lack real analogies from our lifestyle; and therefore find it necessary to rely on crude correspondences to our experience such as "the rope ladder." I do not, for example, know how to describe the stringy piece of ground which has woven itself through the ladder. Nor can I account for the way in which the ladder itself seems to .have no beginning or end, but is part of the ground.

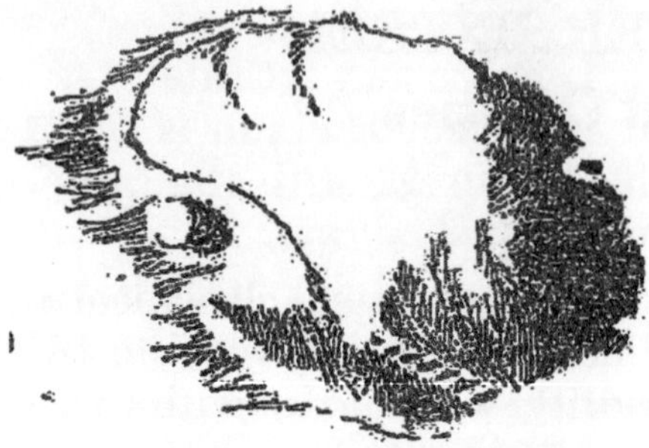

It is possible that this oddity is related to the general strangeness of the Moon's surface to which we have previously alluded. Not only is there a large grid pattern sharply defined in some' places, the Moon also appears to have a smaller pattern of filaments which cross one another at, right angles to form a mesh. At least one qualified person has argued that the skin of the Moon beneath a superficial layer of breccia and dust may actually be an artificial protective cover—a cover which has been exposed in some places due to a horrendous debacle which took place a long time ago.

Have you ever kicked over an anthill and watched the mega-myriad creatures work feverishly to repair? Is this the activity which we are glimpsing on the Moon?

Intelligence in the Form of Pure Energy?

I must be honest and admit that I was—at first—going to leave this out. There is little to go on, and a lot of problems associated with trying to comment on it or describe it. But this is supposed to be an "open book," inviting interpretations, so let me share the problems with you. (How much better it would have been if NASA had shared its problems of interpretation with us!)

The Apollo 16 camera took an eerie bird's-eye-view picture of a vast area northwest of King Crater. It is plate 23

(72-H-1113). Lobachevsky Crater is the most conspicuous one included. The sun is coming from the left side of the pictures, with the interior rim of Lobachevsky mostly in shadow.

But a band of brilliant light stretches from several miles outside the crater to the rim, over the rim, and down to the crater floor.

This band of light is not a ray, such as those which surround Tycho and Copernicus and Kepler, and it is not a patch of reflected light on the ground, one having higher albedo than usual. Neither of these look anything like the oddity I describe. What it does look like is my conception of a band of pure energy moving over the crater rim toward the center of the crater.

The crater is well named: Lobachevsky, for the noted mathematician. Higher math teaches us that the mass of matter going at the speed of light becomes infinite and turns into pure energy. Correspondingly, and still theoretically, pure energy can become matter. Some scientists have speculated that it would be possible to travel between galaxies as pure energy and then re-form into matter at the end of the trip.

This band of light is like no other light one usually sees on the Moon. It maintains its integrity as a light even inside the rim of the crater which is in shadow. (I told you there were problems!) The sides of the band of light are generally straight, and the topography beneath the band shows through. It is a total mystery to me, and I put it down in that column. (But I can't help wondering, why couldn't intelligence be in the form of pure energy?)

Set of Wagon Wheels Half Buried in Sand

That's what it looks like. A better guess would be that it is a servomechanism control or device for making a mechanical change (such as an automatic cover) in the crater.

It is sketched at the top of page 177. One instinctively knows that the crater is "different" by virtue of the black circles on the rim. It is near the Fra Mauro landing site of the Apollo 14 mission. The picture was taken by Orbiter III and is plate 24 (70-H-1630).

If the occupants of the Moon conduct most of Their business of living underground, to escape radiation and meteorites and to maintain ideal temperature, pressure, and atmosphere, then openings to these underground vaults must exist. This crater may represent such an opening— with a control gadget so that precious air will not escape. The black circles parked on the rim may be small private flying vehicles. These guesses may well be wrong, but we can say with a high degree of certainty that the object in that crater was manufactured by very intelligent beings.

More Machinery in a Crater

Two magnificent machine-tooled specimens! And how these creatures do love craters! (An analogous question now arises: what, then, of Mars and Mercury, which also have pockmarked surfaces?

We begin with plate 25 (67-H-304)r It is a dark mare area, near a broad low dome. The crater in question is only about a hundred yards in diameter—one of the smaller anomalous craters we've considered. The area is the Sea of Tranquility, on the near side of the Moon. The crater in question is sketched below.

What can you say about that kind of precision? No doubt you have noticed the portion of a perfect square etched in blackness. Increasingly it becomes apparent that the openings (to vast underground vaults?) take the form of perfect squares, diamonds, etc. It is the least you would expect of an intelligent race.

The next "machine-tooled" specimen combines the metallic object crossing the crater with the partial-covering phenomenon. That is, when the camera took (he picture, the crater was in the process of being covered over. Lintels had begun to move across the expanse of crater to hold up the cover fabric.

This is pictured in plate 26 (7Q-H-1629). The area is also the near side of the Moon. The crater in question is small—on the same order of size as the one considered above. It looks like this:

Two Control Wheels in a Crater

Plate 27 (67-H-41) is loaded with strange craters, but the onelnTEe center stands out. In addition to the familiar object crossing the center of the crater (which perhaps, with similar objects w'hich will emerge from the sides, will hold up a covering), there is a striking control wheel which looks like the head and part of the shank of a screw.

Plumbing? Entrance to an underground community?

I'm beginning to think NASA features these photos with the attitude "Here they are. If you—the public, the scientific fraternity, the press·—are too disinterested or blind to sees these oddities, that's your problem. We're not budgeted to educate you. We barely have enough for our missions."

But let's return to another photo, plate 24, for a second example of a control wheel. It is so perfect and striking that I have sketched it below.

Again, it is a smallish crater, on the near side of, the Moon. Do you notice a pattern in the kinds of anomalies existing on different portions of the Moon? . The cultural anthropologists might have a field day studying the different modes of existence there.

Black Diamonds Are Trumps

We come now to the prize crater·which·is·an·artificial· opening. It is so perfect, so obviously engineered, that if this had been the only phenomenon coming to my attention, I'd have shouted "Eureka!" It is pictured in plate 28 (67-H-266) and, of course, is of an area on this side of the Moon. The crater in question is small, on the order of a hundred yards in diameter. It looks like this. (See below)

If you are curious and have more than a passing interest in this subject, I encourage you to get a copy of this photo and examine it for yourself. (See Appendix for details on how to order.) It is in the area also where Surveyor I soft-landed on the Moon on June 2, 1966. Perhaps you will recall that when we discussed the service-station- on-the-Moon crater near where Ranger Seven impacted, the speculation was offered that NASA had programmed the spacecraft to home in on heat, metal, gas, or something else which might be representative of intelligent activity.

I think that the fact that Surveyor I landed near this anomalous crater is indicative of the quality of that speculation.

Note that the lintels crossing or about to cross this crater are at the level of the inner opening, not the outer. Also that the inner diamond-shaped opening is positioned with an interesting regularity vis-a-vis the outer opening. Without actually viewing the action, it is perfectly obvious that the inner lens of this crater can be closed completely. The blackness there is attributable only to the depth of the opening and not to shadow from the rim. The straight sides opposite each other are parallel, as well as having the same degree of arc, and thus are worth noting. Also, some of the small craterlets surrounding the larger crater have a blurred aspect, as though ground had been thrown up out of the crater to the rim.

Finally, another pattern begins to become apparent: individuality is shown in these anomalous craters, perhaps as a means of identification. Although the craters are alike in their degree of oddity, and the extent to which they show evidence of intelligent engineering, no two appear to be exactly alike in the manner in which this engineering and architecture is carried out. If this crater in question were my abode, I would have no difficulty in finding it as I skimmed low over the Moonscape.

Construction on the Surface of the Moon

The astronauts (as the tapes show) marveled at the sights they saw on the Moon, especially the more or less obvious constructions. They had code words (e.g., "Barbara" and "Annbell") for these and other anomalous sights. They talked about mountains carved into exact shapes, parallel tracks leading right up to what seemed to be constructed walls, and so on.

Plate 29 (67-H-935) contains such a phenomenon. There are parallel walls, with an arch between them, and the sun streams beneath the arch. There are nodes or raised markings located at exactly symmetrical spots on one wall—< each node on a line with the inside line of the two walls, each an exact distance from the corner, each with the same size shadow.

Another construction brings to mind the line "Alabaster cities gleam." It is a beautifully shaped dome on top of an architected platform. The platform is as perfect as though drawn by the most meticulous draftsman. It is sketched later. (Page 183)

There are two pictures of this area, from different perspectives, 71-H-1300 and plate 30 (71-H-1765). This area is one of the most interesting on the Moon, with dozens of mountain masses lining a long valley and many constructions. Figure 1 shows the dome in relief, with only an edge of the foundation showing. Figure 2 can be confusing, as the dome blends in with the white background of the platform. This second picture was taken by the spacecraft camera when the spacecraft was closer to the dome. ("Dome" in this context does not refer to the natural feature astronomers call domes. The latter are perhaps the result of volcanic swelling of other stresses of the Moon's mantle. They tend to be low and irregular, and often have a craterlet at the summit.)

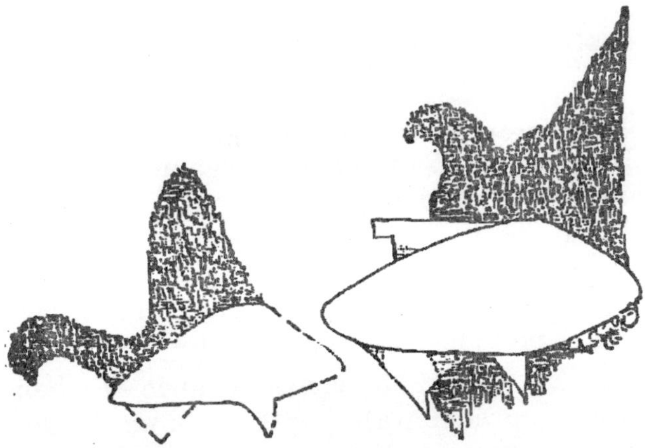

Another example of construction catches the builders in the middle of their job. The skeleton of a vast covering, seven by four miles in area, shows up in plate 31 (69-H-737). All over the Moon there are coverings of one sort or another. Riblike markings show clearly, and the places where the cover material is stretched taut (much like tent canvas when it is stretched) are highlighted by the sun. The ribs of the covering under consideration look like this:

Five parallel ribs (about seven miles in length, tip to tip) can be seen, rising at perhaps a thirty-degree angle and then leveling, all at the identical point, to run horizontally for an equivalent distance. It would be interesting to know what the material which will cover this skeleton is made of. Logic dictates that it will be impervious to dangerous rays (if the unscreened sun's rays are dangerous- to them) and to the impact of small meteorites. Or perhaps these coverings are merely first-line-of-defense safety factors to protect or hide underground communities. Your guess may be as good as mine or that of the analysts at NASA; nobody has been there. None of us, that is.

Filling Up the Storage Tanks or Taking Away the Waste?

They use the "syringe" principle, judging by, photographic evidence, to either empty a load of water into an underground storage tank or suck up wastes for removal to another location. .

Plate 12 (72-H-839) contains evidence of crater sprays, ridges being knocked down, enormous X-drones slaving for their masters. Small wonder, then, that bits of evidence about their maintenance problems show up.

A few miles from the end of that notorious ridge on

which so much work is focused one can find a small ponding effect—looking as though gray sludge had been smoothed over and then jelled. In the middle of this ponding effect are two puffy orbs between a quarter and a half mile in diameter. On one of the orbs can be seen a nipple- like extrusion which is reaching into a craterlet.

Below are sketched the two objects. The one on the left is sticking its nozzle into the craterlet to unload its cargo or to suck up waste; the one on the right (of about the same diameter) is apparently just loafing, in between jobs.

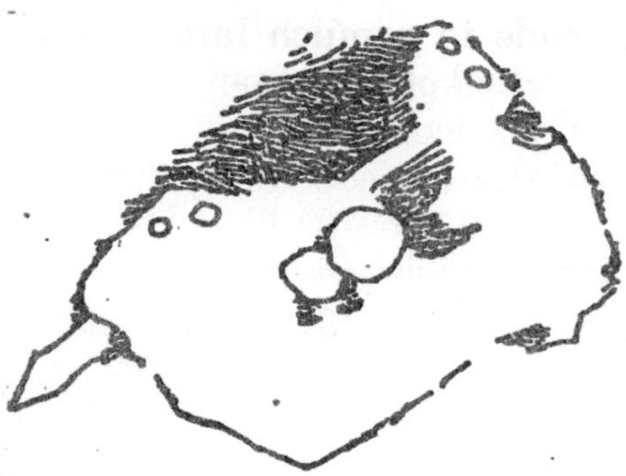

What do They do with Their wastes? Although we have no clear evidence, there are many possibilities, all of which do credit to an advanced face. They can (1) lug them to a central point for re-cycling; (2) place un-recyclables into the Lagrangian Points of the Moon (See Chapter Seventeen for an explanation of these points); or (3) dump them over the friendly skies of Earth, where animals and bacteria and vegetation take care of them. (Remember the falls from the sky of blood and fish—of practically everything flora and fauna—brought to our attention by Charles Fort.) Of course, there are other possibilities. The only thing I am sure of is that the Moon contains no litter, except that left by us.

T-bar Plumbing

We return to smallish craters, many of which show evidence of right-angled and T-bar plumbing. The word "plumbing" is used in its broadest implications: plumbing for water, for wastes, or as a pipelike conduit for a wide variety of basic needs, including atmosphere, heat, fuel, etc.

A clear example shows up in plate 32 (66-H-1611). It is sketched below. The reason for T-bar plumbing of this sort to extrude in a much larger crater (the total length of the sketched object is perhaps a twentieth the crater diameter) is not clear. But since the crater appears to be of the impact variety and not artificial, the plumbing object could have been exposed by accident when the meteorite hit. The resemblance to the object in plate 33 (67-H-318) is striking.

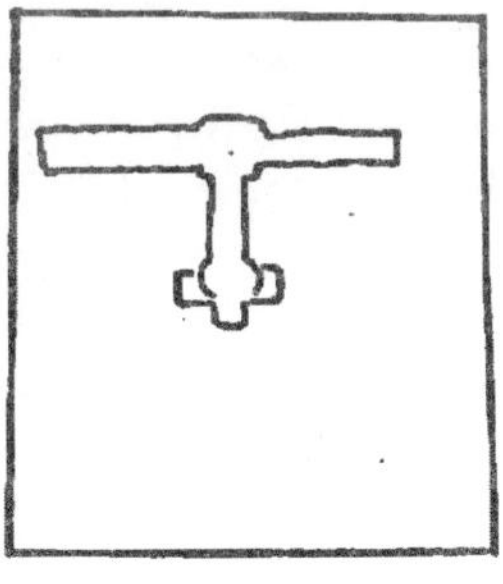

Another type makes its appearance in plate 34 (67-H-307). My sketch of it appears below. The crater in which it is found is very small, not larger than an ordinary house. As would be expected, the area contains many small anomalous craters which are difficult to classify. The "pipe" in the crater under discussion has a sharply defined and perfect right angle, the most persuasive evidence of its artificiality.

Plate 33 contains another beautiful example found at the bottom of a small crater. It is sketched below. The object is of such perfect design that it must be of intelligent origin.

Pipeline conduits and plumbing T-bars are not rare on the Moon. One can scarcely examine a close surface shot which contains smallish craters and not find one. It seems so logical, too, for underground conduit systems to be exposed at intervals; ease of access would be a prime reason. Instead of weekly calls by the "Dempster Dumpster," flying objects come regularly to remove or replenish. Indeed, the Moon, instead of being the dead, barren place we superficially see, is the home of most complex cultures, which are not merely using it for a temporary base, but are established for the long haul.

Of Sculptured Platforms and Gleaming Domes

Saved for last in this chapter is the Disneyland of the Moon—the .Alpine Valley. It could logically have been included in the section called "*Construction on the Surface of the Moon,*" but so compelling and exciting is this area that it deserves to be considered by itself.

The Alpine Valley is on the near side of the Moon, always facing us. It is near the extreme northern edge, neighbor to Plato Crater, where a "blizzard of lights" and other puzzling things are seen. Construction shown in plate 29 (67-H-935) is also at the edge of the Moon, near the Rook Mountains and Schickard Crater in the southeast region. Extending the coincidence, the "domes on platforms" shown in this chapter are also on the very edge of the Moon (as we' see it from Earth), just beyond the Ocean of Storms in the eastern region. One wonders if these above-the-ground builders chose locations almost out of our view but where they nonetheless could keep watch on us on Their horizon!

The Alpine Valley is an area of contrasts. A resident of one of the habitats high up on a sculptured platform has a view out on a broad flat mare, or plain; in another direction there are mountains; and everywhere there are the carved aesthetics so tied to his existence.

There are suggestions that the occupants of the Alpine Valley live above the ground, unlike the occupants of many other areas of the Moon, where underground dwellings seem fashionable. They live above the ground in domes and other sculptured geometries carved on top of gleaming flat platforms. (One must wonder if the Alpine Valley residents and those living in that other dome-on-a-platform structure discussed earlier in this chapter are not home-town siblings! The modes of existence are certainly similar.

The imagination which was used to develop the many platforms and domes is impressive. It is as though we on Earth brought together our most creative artists and said, "Here is a thousand-square-mile plot of mountains and prairies. Do with it as you will," and then we backed them up with giant carvers and earthmovers to carry out their whims.

Does the structure resting on a platform in the sketch below intrigue you? Clearly, aesthetics is an important part of this space race's existence. There is intelligence and artistic ability here. Sometimes (judging by the literature) we imagine intelligent space races to be all purpose and brain, and rarely consider that they may possess highly developed senses of humor and artistry. Looking at this object cheers me much.

There are at least three different photos of the Alpine Valley. Plate 35 (67-H-897) is not the crispest, but is the most revealing. The other two photos are 67-H-1409 and 67-H-1400. 67-H-897 is presented for your attention.

One person hypothesizes that the domed structure on the platform (see above) is not an abode but a spaceship. He believes the platform is a spaceport. However, it shows up in the same position in ail three pictures, two of which were taken three months apart. If it were a spaceship, ii seems possible (though not necessarily likely) that some change would be shown: the ship would have changed position, or even be absent in one of the pictures.

But there is a more compelling reason for calling the structure an abode instead of a spaceship. It is that the area is filled with ovals and circles rising to beautiful geometric peaks. The particular culture which chose the Alpine Valley clearly likes the view from high platforms. None of these structures has shown change from one picture to the other—at least, none which I have noticed. But there is no compelling reason why change at that distance and size would show up. If you consider only objects the size of an office building or larger, then views from the air over an American city might show no change over a period of three months.

After studying the Alpine Valley, one is tempted to say that almost none of the mountains and enormous plateaus are of natural origin—or at least have not remained in their natural state. Platform after gleaming platform is there, each with its own brand of dome. They are all about the same size: in the vicinity of two miles wide. The shape and size of the shadows they cast lead me to estimate their height at about half a mile. The platform in the sketch is six miles across at its widest point.

Do you know how big a community one dome that size could maintain? Obviously, an entire American town could be placed inside one, with enough room left over for hydroponic farming and hobby indulgence. Atmospheric pressure and breathable air could be easily maintained. The dome, as Earth engineers have discovered, is a practical and efficient building shape, with considerable strength.

Here are sketches of some other interesting platforms and structures in the Alpine Valley. All of the platforms range in size from six to ten miles across, while the dome structures are of an identical size. The source of the sketches is plate 35.

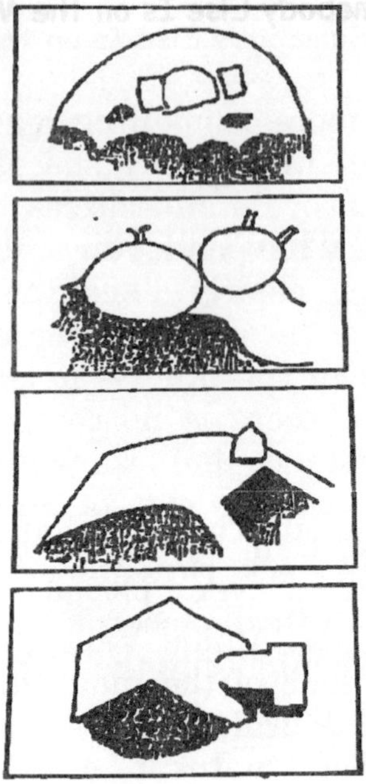

And Damon Knight, in his biography of Charles Fort, Prophet of the Unexplained (Doubleday, 1970), quotes Thomas Kuhn's Structure of Scientific Revolutions: "In science . . . novelty emerges only with difficulty, manifested by resistance, against a background provided by expectation. Initially, only the anticipated and usual are experienced even under circumstances where anomaly is later to be observed."

CHAPTER SEVENTEEN
When Is a Moon Not a Moon?

My friend Lew called. The information business at HEW must have been slack. He sounded excited.

"There are at least fifteen objects flying ahead of and behind Jupiter!" he shouted into the phone.

I pushed aside the photos of Tycho and prepared for a long siege.

"You there, George?"

"Right here, Lew."

"I said there are these things..

"Yeah, Lew." The number 15 was a clue. I believed I knew what he meant. "There are special points sixty degrees ahead and behind a smaller object revolving around a much larger one. The ratio of size has to be a little more than twenty-eight to one. They call these Lagrangian Points. All the planets revolving around the sun have them. So does our Moon. You can stick something in one of these Lagrangian Points and it might stay there forever—or as long as the planets do."

"Let's get back to Jupiter."

"We're getting there. The thing is that asteroids, all kinds of space junk and dust, can collect in these Lagrangian Points and not get swept up by the gravitational attractions of bigger bodies. About fifteen asteroids have been spotted at these points ahead and behind Jupiter. There's probably lots more that can't be seen with the telescopes. Those what you mean, Lew?"

"Asteroids!" Lew snorted. "You call them asteroids!"

I tried to focus my eyes on the picture of Tycho, could not. "Okay, Lew. What would you call them?"

Hesitation. "They could be anything. Even spaceships." 191

"But there's absolutely no reason to assume . .

"That's the trouble with you people into astronomy'," Lew said. "Afraid to make an assumption. Afraid, to stick your neck out. The plain truth is none of you know what those damn things are. Admit it."

"Lew," I began slowly. (Into astronomy? Wasn't it the other way around?) "The solar system is loaded with planetary bodies. There are small planets nobody's seen or dreamed of yet. Ever heard of the asteroid belt? Countless chunks of rock and metal going around the sun. And a long time ago there were millions more of them orbiting the sun and the bigger planets. A lot of them got captured or crashed into the giants. Those left, outside of the asteroid belt, are in the safer spots where they can't easily get swept up. They call these asteroids caught in the Lagrangian Points Trojans."

"Sure," Lew said. "Isn't that what science is all about? Naming things? Got to have a name for them."

"Now if you were to report that someone has found asteroids trapped in the Moon's Lagrangian Points, that would be news." I was a little piqued. "And a hell of a lot more interesting. Everybody knows about the Trojans leading and chasing Jupiter."

Silence. I'd gotten to him, and I didn't like it.

"Isaac. Asimov has a proposal," I said quickly. "It seems to me the most creative to come along since they planned the first Moon shots. He says we should take, our radioactive wastes and shoot them into the two stable Lagrangian Points associated with the Earth-Moon system. That way, they wouldn't be around to make trouble for future generations. What they do now with dangerous wastes is bury them deep or put them in a concrete casket and dump them out at sea. The time it will take for those caskets to disintegrate can be calculated."

Lew made sounds of listening.

"Asimov calls these two points—the Langrangian Points storing radioactive wastes—the 'Trojan hearse,' I said. But I don't think Lew appreciated Asimov's pun. He mumbled something and hung up.

Moons in the solar system. Strange things. We accept them as being perfectly natural, part of the natural scheme of things, but maybe they aren't. I sat long after Lew hung up thinking about them—about what I'd read and heard. The Subject grabbed me so much that I forgot for half an hour about the new photos sitting on my desk.

The truth is, we do not know a lot about moons. We don't know where they come from, what' they are, why some behave so differently from others. The Apollo 17 Preliminary Science Report put out by NASA says in its introduction, "Yet, despite the great strides taken in knowledge about the Moon, its origin and formation are still unknown."

And some of what we once knew we forget. We kid ourselves and new generations that the moons of the solar system constitute a stable setup, that they have been as they are now since the beginning of time.

Bull.

You think the moons of Jupiter revolve around the planet like clockwork? Then be advised that astronomers found, all down through the nineteenth century, that certain of the satellites did not appear from behind the disc of Jupiter on time. One would disappear behind the planet and then be several minutes late in showing again.

Sometimes, when one of Jupiter'.s satellites was

supposed to be in plain sight, it could not be seen at all.

Cassini, one of the great names in astronomy, saw a satellite orbiting Venus in 1672. It was seen by other astronomers and scientists: James Short, Tobias Mayer, Montaigne. It was seen repeatedly from 1672 to 1764. Its orbit a was calculated, its distance from Venus estimated. It had an apparent diameter of two thousand miles. After 1764 it was never seen again. Astronomers today agree that Venus has no moon.

Everyone today is familiar with the story of how Asaph Hall discovered the two tiny moons of Mars in 1877, after many competent people had looked in vain for a satellite over a long period. Stranger still, however, is the story of how Phobos and Deimos had been written about generations earlier by others, including Jonathan Swift, who had come close to describing them accurately. *It sounds improbable, but the empirical evidence indicates that two chunks of rock began orbiting Mars for the first time in 1877 -- or came back after having once been there in the past.* An interesting and pertinent sidelight is that the Mariner shots taken by NASA reveal a bottle-mouth opening of a crater on Phobos; an opening so perfect in its detail that the artificial origin of the Martian moos becomes believable.

As another sidelight, NASA's volume Mars as Viewed b? Mariner 9 contains this interesting paragraph in a chapter entitled "Mysterious Canyons": "The major obstacle to any convincing explanation of the origin of the canyons is: How was the bulk of the material originally present in these enormous chasms removed? There is no obvious way to transport debris out except by the wind. Yet the amount of material to be transported is so great as to cast doubt on the effectiveness of this mechanism operating by itself. The disposal of such vast amounts of material remains a problem." These canyons are up to two hundred kilometers wide, thousands of kilometers long, and possibly as much as six kilometers deep.

Phobos orbits Mars in less than one-third the time it takes Mars to rotate once. This makes Phobos unique in the solar system. Deimos, the outer moon, takes about five and one-half hours more per revolution than the primary planet takes to rotate. The Russian astronomer I. Shlovskii (and others) suggested that both of these Martian moons are artificial, put into orbit in the early 1870s. An astronomer named E. Holden, who succeeded Dr. Asaph Hall at the Washington Observatory, reported a third satellite of Mars, which moved in contradiction to Kepler's Third Law of Motion. The satellite is not recognized by others.

Uranus has five official satellites. Two of them were discovered by Herschel, the English astronomer who first found Uranus itself. Lest you think that astronomers in the late 1700s were unequipped, the fact is that Herschel built a reflecting telescope of 48-inch aperture! He devoted eight years to the search for other satellites. He thought he had found four more—farther away from the "primary planet than the additional three discovered later. Nobody has ever found a trace of these moons of Uranus which Herschel saw. They have never been seen again.

Ever heard of Vulcan? It was the name of a planet discovered in 1762 and reported by a host of astronomers for the next century. The orbit of Vulcan was calculated. It was infra-Mercurian—that is, inside the orbit of Mercury, closer to the sun. Such men of note as Schmidt, Wolf, Hoffman, Leverrier (discoverer of Neptune), Lescarbault, and many others saw it. Leverrier, after long observation, calculated that the best time for seeing Vulcan would be on March 22, 1877.

There was no Vulcan on that day. The last observation was in 1876. This was about the period of the appearance of the two moons of Mars and two years before two infra- Mercurian bodies were independently discovered by Swift and Watson. Lewis Swift, director of the Warner Observatory in Rochester, discovered over 1200 nebulae and twelve comets. James C. Watson, director of Washburn Observatory at the University of Wisconsin, discovered twenty-two asteroids. Professor Watson assured Dr. Asaph Hall that he and Swift had seen the two luminous objects independently, and precisely identified their positions, without knowledge of each other's discovery. Nonetheless, Professor Colbert, Superintendent of Dearborn Observatory, attacked the integrity of the two men. Nobody has ever seen what these sophisticated astronomers had described. The two bodies passed into limbo.

This also closely approximated the time of the so-called incredible decade.

Isaac Asimov says there are nine moons in our solar system which have been captured: one of Neptune, one of Saturn, and seven of Jupiter. He bases this on what he calls the "tug-of-war" ratio: the attraction of the planet versus the attraction of the sun. This ratio ranges from Miranda, a satellite of Uranus, which has a tug-of-war ratio of 24,600, to the seventh moon of Jupiter, which has a ratio of 1.03. He calls the other satellites "true satellites."

And then he comes to our Moon. It is important to quote him:

"It is a shame that one small thing remains unaccounted for; one trifling thing I have ignored so far. but— WHAT IN BLAZES IS OUR OWN MOON DOING WAY OUT THERE? It's too far out to be a true satellite of Earth, if we go by my beautiful chain of reasoning—which is too beautiful for me to abandon. It's too big to have been captured by the Earth. The chances of such a capture having been effected and the Moon then having taken up a nearly circular orbit about the Earth are too small to make such an eventuality credible.

There are theories, of course, to the effect that the Moon was once much closer to the Earth (within my permitted limits for a true satellite) and then gradually moved away as a result of tidal action. Well, I have an objection to that. If the Moon were a true satellite that originally had circled Earth at a distance of, say, 20,000 miles, it would almost certainly be orbiting in the plane of Earth's equator and it isn't.

But, then, if the Moon is neither a true satellite of the Earth nor a captured one, what is it?..." *

He goes on to calculate the tug-of-war ratio for the Moon: 0.46. We would lose the tug of war with the sun. We—Earth—attract the Moon half as strongly as does the Sun. Asimov solves the problem by indicating that another category exists: that of double planetary systems. The Earth-Moon system is a double planetary one. The only problem with this is that Apollo flights of NASA seem to show that the Moon did not evolve along with Earth, that it had an entirely, different history. Dr. Harold C. Urey believes that the Moon was captured by Earth. He says, *"It is difficult to understand how the Moon acquired such a different composition from that of the Earth especially with respect to metallic iron. . . . The Earth has a large iron core and the Moon, at most, only a very small one."* **

You put your money down and take your choice. The only thing we're sure of is that the Moon is pretty weird.

Laplace formulated a theory in which all the moons and planets and the sun were supposed to fit: one original motion caused them all to rotate and revolve in the same direction. *But Velikovsky pointed out that one of the moons of Saturn and the moon of Neptune and several moons of Jupiter all revolve in the opposite direction from the main solar system thrust.*

* Isaac Asimov, Asimov on Astronomy, Mercury Press, Inc., 1963

** Harold C. Urey, "The Moon and Its Origin," Part of Section "The New Moon: Part 1," Bulletin of the Atomic Scientists, November, 1973.

(One of Saturn, one of Neptune, several of Jupiter. Does this sound like Asimov's estimate of captured moons?)

Laplace wrote: "One finds by the analysis of the probabilities that there are more than four thousand billion chances to one that this arrangement [i.e., the movement of planets and moons in the same direction] is not the result of chance; this probability is considered higher than that of the reality of historical events with regard to which no one would venture a doubt."

Moons which come and go over the years.

Moons which are late in appearing as they revolve around their parent.

Moons which go in the opposite direction from the general movement of the solar system.

Moons which orbit a planet which has already lost the tug-of-war with the sun—and which are too big to have been captured.

A Moon which is being feverishly worked by myriad occupants.

Can it be that macro-spaceships exist in the solar system —ships which can be driven anywhere? Spaceships which use the orbit patterns of larger planets as parking places? (Was Arthur Clarke right about the first moon of Jupiter, and was Shlovskii right about the inner moon of Mars?)

And J. B. S. Haldane, the biologist who explored genetics and ethics as well, said: "The universe is not only queerer than we suppose, but queerer than we can suppose."

CHAPTER EIGHTEEN
Polling It All Together: Some Hypotheses

How could we reveal to beings on another planet that some of us on Earth are highly intelligent? What would somebody on Mars or Venus, looking through a telescope, have to see to be convinced?

In his magnificent book We Are Not Alone (McGraw-Hill, 1964), Walter Sullivan relates how various scientists in the past have proposed to reveal our presence:

• The mathematician Karl Friedrich Gauss suggested that forest lanes be planted in Siberia to form a gigantic right-angled triangle; squares could be erected on each side to illustrate the Pythagorean theorem. (The square of the hypotenuse equals the sum of the squares of the other two sides.)

• The astronomer Joseph Johann von Littrow urged that canals be dug in the Sahara, forming geometric figures twenty miles on a side; at night kerosene could be spread over the water and lighted.

• The French scientist Charles Cros wanted his government to construct a vast mirror to reflect sunlight to Mars.

• Bernard M. Oliver, electronics engineer, told the American Institute of Aeronautics and Astronautics that intelligent radio signals are probably pouring in on Earth undetected. He urged the construction of sensitive equipment to listen. And Nikola Tesla wanted us to send radio waves which intelligent beings will recognize as nonrandom patterns. Both listening and sending are now being done.

And when we come up against intelligent life on another planet, it is assumed we will first be aware of Them through Their works: what They do, what They build. The above suggestions are all based on the idea of revealing Earth people's existence through demonstrations of intelligent configurations, which could be vegetation, water, mirrors, or radio waves.

Patterns. Geometricities. Straight lines. It is assumed that a triangle (isosceles, equilateral, or right-angled) will reveal the existence of our brains, and it will. But then we turn around and ignore exactly this and a thousand even more convincing patterns on the Moon. This is science?

In this book I have considered the patterns made by alien beings on the Moon. Their patterns include practically all geometric designs plus rigs, ground markings, insignia and glyphs, constructions for moving around and living and working.

We have seen Their presence, the patterns of Their behavior, through dust being kicked up, lights and flaxes, sprays coming out of dozens of small craters, gas under pressure ejected from discrete nozzles, rays streaming from craters which They continually visit, vehicle tracks, and electromagnetic wave towers on top of the highest peaks.

We have seen pipes and conduits, gears, stitches holding together pieces of the Moon's crust, large coverings and the ribs which hold them up, and objects which could even be a form of life itself.

These data have clearly shown up in a limited number of pictures made available by NASA, following a limited amount of study and research performed primarily by one person. What would a really systematic search of the Moon's surface produce? How far has NASA gone?

Amitai Etzioni pointed out in an editorial in Science

(Oct. 23, 1970) that some societies (e.g., France and Germany before World War II) were shy on collection of facts but long on analysis and theories, while the American system is heavily oriented toward fact-finding but short on analysis. Funds for the collection of data are much more readily available than for their interpretation. Pragmatism finds raw fact more appealing than the speculation about its meaning. The net result is a national science-information "system which knows more about the trees than the forest, which is well informed about specifics but lacks a comprehensive, systematic overview.

One group contributing perhaps more than any other to this state of affairs is the National Academy of Sciences. While it is not the most progressive organization in the country, it does have the most scientific prestige and power. Some think of it as an important adviser to government agencies and Congress, and others view it as a "self-perpetuating honor society for outstanding scientists." If we substitute the word "Pentagon" for "government agencies and Congress," then both opinions are true.

Scratch a scientist and you will find a human being wanting to get elected to the Academy. Scratch a member and you will find a person who wants at all costs to protect his/her status. (There are noteworthy exceptions.)

Criteria for election are supposed to include original, creative scientific research. But, as Philip Boffey points out in his article "The Lords of Science" (Potomac Magazine, June 22, 1975), the Academy has seen fit to reject some candidates who are achievers in the eyes of the public, as well as others who seemed qualified. The scientific establishment has never looked benignly on those scientists who communicate directly with people outside the pages of accepted journals or scientific meeting halls. James R. Killian, a former Presidential science adviser and M.I.T. president, never made it. Neither did Jonas Salk. The list of those who created waves, "went public," or did not come from the major universities and then failed to make the Academy is long. Nobel Prize winners (perhaps at the pinnacle of public exposure) usually get elected after winning the prize.

One can easily guess where the National Academy of Sciences stands on the very serious issue of UFOs, despite the demonstrable scientific evidence proving their existence. And if it rejects UFOs, you can be sure the Academy 'will have no comment on the thesis of this book. (Notwithstanding the fact that some members have been known to discuss the thesis of this book in private.) If the government doesn't tell you about it, would the Academy? Boffey quotes Stewart L. Udall, former Secretary of the Interior, as saying that the Academy functions "all too often as a virtual puppet of government... a mere adjunct of established institutions," dutifully providing "a convenient rationale for the SST lobby, the highway contractors, and the Defense Department" (italics added). If the Defense Department and its superiors in the intelligence group call the shots in the area of extraterrestrial intelligence, and you are a scientist aching to gain the shelter and prestige of the Academy, and at the same time you have this healthy

curiosity about UFOs and the phenomena on the Moon .. . Well, how are you going to behave?

I quote Boffey—and bear in mind that he is talking about the highest, most prestigious scientific council in the land:

"The Academy did little to alert the nation to the dangers of nuclear fallout; it made no contribution to the national debate over whether to build an antiballistic missile system; it offered no counsel on most other arms control issues; and it has had very little impact on crime, the drug culture, and worsening urban and rural conditions. Nor has the Academy

played a lead role in the energy crisis, nuclear reactor safety, automobile safety, the environmental movement, or the improvement of health care."

All of these problems have definite implications for science. What is the Academy supposed to advise on? What's it supposed to do?

So the data-gathering goes on and the important analysis and advice in critical matters gets short shrift. Frederick J, Hooven, a Dartmouth professor, has commented: "Speculation is so firmly discouraged in science that scientists genet ally show no talent for it, or more probably they are inhibited by fear of ridicule or disapproval by their colleagues" (Saturday Review, March 29, 1969). Before a scientific breakthrough can be made, somebody must speculate and form a hypothesis.

With speculation frowned upon, the National Academy of Sciences recognizing only orthodox values and maintaining a subservience to the Defense Department, and scientists mesmerized by the Academy and their own need for status, one can justifiably ask: is it surprising that the phenomena on the Moon have not been officially reported? Is it fair, considering how we generally vote our pocket- books in national elections, to expect scientists to cut their own throats?

Some scientists make brave speculative statements. Usually they make them early in their careers. Carl Sagan speculated in the early 1960s that extraterrestrials might have a base on the hidden side of the Moon. It might, he suggested, have been placed there ages ago to provide continuity for expeditions to Earth. He said that we should keep in mind, as we later examined high-resolution photographs of the Moon, the possibility of such a base. (This was reported by Walter Sullivan in *We Are Not Alone.*)

The bases are there. On the other side of the Moon and on the near side. They are around King Crater, in or under a thousand small craters with no names, in places east of Mare Smythii, Tycho, the Alps—the catalogue would fill pages. These bases will not look like Las Vegas or the Mt. Palomar complex. We must get out of the old ways of thinking. Why doesn't Dr. Sagan speak out now? Why doesn't he give in to the very human impulse to want to say, "There, see them? I told you so!" But he chooses, whenever he talks on TV or in the lecture hall, to refer with cutting sarcasm to the idea of aliens in the solar system now. One wonders who is calling the shots.

The physicists and astronomers and other scientists will someday get together and decide (for public consumption) that the Moon is occupied. It may not happen for another twenty years. In the meantime, the occupants of the Moon will not feel constrained by Earth orthodoxy. They will keep right on doing whatever they feel it necessary to do. They still exist.

In the meantime, too, an opportunity is afforded a few to analyze the data and develop theories. I look upon this book as a preliminary report, a first approximation of the truth. But it is impossible to go even this far without forming ideas, hypotheses, about the data. The hypotheses included in this chapter have suggestive evidence reinforcing them to varying degrees. They strike, I believe, to the heart of things as we are now beginning to see them.

1. *More than one space race occupies the Moon.*

Culture traits and technology seen in different parts of the Moon vary considerably. We have different cultures among humans on Earth, but they do not really vary much. Russian and American buildings and automobiles are similar in important respects. The world's airplanes look substantially the same.

In contrast, on the Moon there are totally different ways of doing things. In the Tycho area there is not a single example of an X-drone, while parts of the other side of the Moon—notably the King and Guyot Crater areas— abound with them. The Alpine Valley contains many striking examples of architected constructions sitting on high

flat platforms, but I have seen this feature in only one other place on the Moon (in another valley, incidentally, on the Moon's limb).

Crater spraying, too, is a technological culture trait which seems confined to particular areas. High towers on top of peaks are found in the Bullialdus area, not everywhere.

Finally, Their means of transportation differ radically, if well-documented reports of UFOs around the Earth are a criterion and if, indeed, They all use the Moon as an interim base. Consider the extremes: a metallic disc fifteen feet in diameter, creating electromagnetic effects, and a fuzzy globe which seems non-material, changes shape, and descends to poke around Earth installations.

My conclusion is that space races from two or more different planets are on the Moon, and that perhaps They have changed off at intervals: one moves out, another moves in. If we are of interest, or the minerals up there are of interest, then there's reason to assume that more than one race would be interested in the Moon. If extraterrestrial cultures have even the vaguest commonalities with us, then it is to be expected that the same culture will spread its technological fruits dramatically throughout the areas of its domain, as gas expands to fill a vacuum. Locations where a particular culture trait is not seen on the Moon are probably beyond the bounds of that culture's domain.

In short, if the extraterrestrials occupying the Moon have one trait in common with us—the trait of using a basically similar design for the engineered objects of a planet—the above hypothesis must be true.

2. *One major mission of the occupants of the Moon is to extract metals and other rare elements from its crust.*

Evidence lies in the work They are doing.

The Apollo flights, as well as spectrographic analyses and examination of soil and rocks, have shown that iron, nickel, aluminum, titanium, uranium, and thorium are present on the Moon in amounts making extraction practicable. There are dozens of other metals and elements which may be worth taking, depending on the efficiency of the extraction process used, and we have seen that the Moon residents operate on such huge scales that They work on an entirely different order of efficiency than we do.

A relatively old and technologically advanced race on another planet might well have exhausted its native supply of needed basic materials. One can safely assume this will happen to every race at some point in its maturity. Our Earth will be frighteningly short of some raw materials necessary for the support of our huge populations before this century ends. By then (if we still exist) we may be going to other planets, other creatures' moons . . .

3. *The Moon suffered a fantastic catastrophe in space eons ago, and way driven here by its occupants for a. long recup eration-repair job.*

While extremely tenuous, this hypothesis has more to support it than you might think. It is an alternative to hypothesis No. 2.

The Moon is a strange body. Everybody who has studied it agrees on that. In fact, that is about the only thing we have complete agreement on. It does not seem to belong here. Three major hypotheses bandied about for generations (tom out of Earth, formed out of gaseous dusty material alongside the Earth, captured by Earth) have been lacerated separately by various authorities; it depends upon whom you read.

It seems to have a built structure to it—a matrix, a grid-work, a weave. (Recall that an object struck its surface and the Moon vibrated for an hour. The shock waves were recorded by seismographs some distance away.) If you hit bedrock in Peking with a hydraulic hammer, I doubt it would be felt in Pittsburgh; but the same blow on the far side of the Moon would certainly be detected on the near side.

To bring the Moon-was-driven-here-eons-ago hypothesis into the realm of feasibility—away from mere science fiction—let's consider the theories of Parol Froman, once Technical Associate Director of the Los Alamos Scientific Laboratory in New Mexico. Talking to the American Physical Society in 1961, he said that the sun would eventually burn out, and postulated that before that happened Earth- people might be able to push Earth into another solar system. Fusion reactions could power the journey. We could reach star systems 1300 light-years away. And Lyman Spitzer, then head of the Princeton University Observatory, spoke in 1951 of enormous vehicles powered by uranium, capable of carrying thousands of people to other solar systems more hospitable in a time of crisis. Others have mentioned the feasibility of restructuring the entire solar system, redistributing its matter to achieve maximum energy and living space.

A space race with five thousand years of advanced technology behind it (we have perhaps a hundred) would clearly find driving the Moon to another solar system less of a challenge than our first thoughts indicate.

Also supporting this hypothesis is the length of time (at least three thousand years) that our legends tell us the extraterrestrials have been visiting us; the vast repair and "pushing the Moon around" going on; the evenly spaced identical-sized stitches seen holding parts of the Moon's skin together; and the rough contours of evidence we have on Earth for calamitous changes in the solar system during the millennium before Christ. A body the size and mass of the Moon would have to create disruptions even if it were driven into our orbit with precision and the utmost care. Every planet, particularly the inner planets—from Mercury to Mars—would be noticeably affected.

4. *The occupants of the Moon have been engaged in a long-term breeding experiment, beginning with the development of Homo sapiens through genetic tinkering and/or crossbreeding great apes with an extraterrestrial hominoid and continuing with periodic infusions to guard against mental retrogression.*

This hypothesis, an alternative to hypothesis No. 2, is not new. Many writers have developed it, to varying degrees and in various ways. The Lorenzens touch upon it in Flying Saucer Occupants, in which numerous cases involving examination and mating are reviewed. "The possibility that the Villas-Boas affairs was in actuality a breeding experiment is logically although not emotionally acceptable to most" (page 206). (Villas-Boas, a young man living in Sao Paulo State, Brazil, was visited, looked over, and examined by several UFO occupants. Later he was taken into a UFO, undressed, left alone in a room filled with a vapor which made him sick, then seduced by a small, slant-eyed, attractive woman. He was judged by authorities to be sane, intelligent, and truthful.)

The Lorenzens cite a geneticist as saying that if the Villas-Boas affair is true, the occupants of the UFOs must be of human ancestry. "*It is an utter impossibility for living organisms of separate evolutions to sexually unite their genes ... it would be impossible . . . unless they were of common genetic background . . .*" The use of such strong terms by a scientist sounds unscientific; if the advanced extraterrestrials once got past the initial breeding experiment, which would be between representatives of two different genetic stocks, then presumably the ensuing efforts would be easier.

The need to watch the experiment, nurse it, could explain the constant visits through the ages. One could explain the Old Testament on the basis of this hypothesis. *"Be fruitful and multiply," "Replenish the earth," "It is better to spill your seed in the belly of a whore than on the ground."* and Biblical injunctions against homosexuality are consistent with the need to breed so that each genetic infusion would get spread far and wide. The ultimate dispersal of the Jews over half the globe could have been engineered in order to spread these genetic changes.

Every culture has its legends of gods arriving in spaceships. They abound in stories of mating experiments. One can postulate that extraterrestrial contacts all over the world were for the express purpose of continuing to change (upgrade? improve?) the human species.

Was Neanderthal man an experiment that did not succeed? He died out, without encouragement. Cro-Magnon man, similar to us. appeared out of nowhere. The anthropologists have never succeeded in explaining him. After he was shown how to grow wheat and herd cattle, his stock began to zoom about 6000 B.C.

Although his remains have been found which date considerably earlier, Cro-Magnon man probably began to flourish in Europe around 30,000-20,000 B.C., at a time when Neanderthal man was dying out, but they did coexist for a period. Cro-Magnon man was taller, straighter, and smarter. Velikovsky asked how the body, brain and mind of man, an enormously sophisticated biological apparatus spanning millions of years of time, was able to produce a recorded history of only a few thousand years (interview with Immanuel Velikovsky in Science and Mechanics, July, 1968). Other writers who question the pap and • orthodoxy given to us as fact in schools have referred to the seeming race amnesia afflicting us. One way to make sense out of these puzzling issues is to consider the possibility that Homo sapiens' mind is a fairly recent phenomenon and is the result of a long genetic trial.

There are many well-documented cases on record which involve the taking of humans on board spacecraft and sticking needles into them. Betty and Barney Hill of Interrupted Journey are well known. The two fishermen in Mississippi who were kidnapped by a UFO and examined received wide publicity. Many cases are not publicized. A handful of these "infusions" in each continent, spread around randomly, could result in almost total genetic absorption by the race in a couple of thousand years.

While the theory of evolution certainly accounts for most of the development of life on our planet, there has always been nagging suspicion that a gap exists where Homo sapiens is concerned. The jump from great-ape ancestor to our ancestor has many questions which are unanswered—especially the question of timing and how our brain was actually developed. This hypothesis provides an alternative rationale for the presence of the Moon's occupants (an alternative to mining), and answers some of the questions about man's past which we do not come to grips with.

Genesis refers to men from the skies mating with Earthwomen. The Incans had legends of giants descending from the clouds and having sexual intercourse with Incan women. Greek mythology related how gods and goddesses came down and consorted with mortals. "And God said, Let us make man in our image," Genesis states (1:26). Why do we sneer at our legends? Why do we construct complex religions, which affect most people's lives, around Biblical concepts and injunctions—and then ignore the genuine hints about our past which the Bible gives us?

The United Nations Economic and Social Council

(UNESCO) sponsored a conference in Paris during the 1960s. Anthropologists, geologists, etc., from thirty-five nations were given the problem: "Who is man and where did he come from?"

Conclusion of the symposium: "The only certainty about the origin of man is that we are uncertain."

The occupants of the Moon may well have the long-" range goal of breeding us toward a given standard. If this is the case, They may be compared to ranchers who establish a camp on the range to infuse their herd with new vigor after buying a prize bull—except the "camp" on the Moon is a lot more permanent and elaborate.

5. *Although the occupants of the Moon are self-sufficient in most respects, it is probable that They are, to some extent, parasitic on Earth.*

The Moon is totally barren, and while hydroponic farming and even herding underground are possible, such necessary items as fertilizer and water are taken from us.

There is observational evidence for the stealing of animals. Before you smile sardonically, read the data; for a start, see the Lorenzens' Flying Saucer Occupants (Signet. 1967), page 99. The Lorenzens are very cautious and thorough observers. Also see the chapter "Cattle Rustlers from the Skies" in Strange Creatures from Time and Space, by John Keel (Fawcett Gold Medal, 1970). And ST one needs is a slight acquaintance with the writings of Charles Fort to fathom out quite an ecology going on up there partially based on flora and fauna taken from the Earth.

The taking of water from lakes in Canada and other less- populated areas of the Earth is too well documented to dispute. Miners, trappers, and fishermen have watched small hominoids leave their discs and put hoses into the fresh water. The Steep Rock Echo (Ontario) for September-October 1950 related that a man and his wife on a fishing trip watched ten small occupants of a UFO take on water through a hose. And John Nicholson reported in Fantastic Universe (May 1958) that on two separate occasions two miners watched tiny creatures take water from the junction of Marble and Jordon Creeks in Butte County, California.

Reports about UFO occupants taking on water usually involve small hominoids who move stiffly, "automaton-like." Frank Edwards related a theory ("Scientists and Satellites," Fate, February, 1958) which held that countless sightings of UFOs were observed over water, and that the UFOs perhaps hauled water up several hundred miles and expelled it into the atmosphere, where it froze and then was towed to the Moon. This could explain the numerous falls. of ice to Earth.

UFO occupants have been seen on the ground examining tobacco and other plants. No part of our agriculture has missed Their inspection. Do They eat what we eat? Do They eat? While this may not be true of all occupants of the Moon, because of the almost inevitable shift to mechanical bodies at some point in their development., there is fragmentary information leading to the guess that either some do, or have creatures working for them which do.

6. *Instead of contradicting others writing in fields touching on extraterrestrials and solar-system events, the thesis of this book tends to provide a unifying link for many of them.*

A linkage is provided with the chief serious writers, on UFOs, of course. These writers include Valley, Hynek, the Lorenzens, and Aime Michel, to name a few of the more reliable.

But I am concerned more, for the purpose of this hypothesis, with those writers developing unique models pr interpretations. While all the following writers did not necessarily accomplish this unilaterally or originally (for example, von Daniken was preceded in his main thesis by F. W. Holiday [Creatures from the Inner Sphere], John Michell [The Flying Saucer Vision], Eric Norman [Goa's, Demons and UFO's, Lancer Books, 1970], Robert Charroux [One Hundred Thousand Years of Man's Unknown History, Berkley Medallion, 1970], and several others, some showing superior scholarship), they tend to be identified with the point of view in the public mind:

von Daniken

- Ancient astronauts came to Earth and left their mark (Chariots of the Gods?).

Velikovsky

- The Moon was repeatedly involved in solar-system catastrophes in the first two millennia B.C., which damaged it and displaced it from its orbit (Worlds in Collision).

Vallee

- Elves, pixies, leprechauns, brownies, etc., have a basis in reality; they might have been remnants of old Earth races, or extraterrestrials (Passport to Magonia).

Berlitz,

- There is an area, bounded by Key West,
  Sander
- Bermuda, and Puerto Rico, in son, et al. which hundreds of ships, planes, etc., have disappeared and where large UFOs have been sighted (The Bermuda Triangle).

Fuller

- Extraterrestrials put a man and his wife in a trance,

took them aboard a UFO, and examined them closely before returning them to their car (The Interrupted Journey).

Ezekiel,

- Numerous people in the ancient world were approached and spoken to by beings who looked like people but who arrived in flying machines and did things far beyond the technology of the time (the Bible).

Fort,

- Ice, blood, vegetation, fish, etc., have been intermittently falling out of the sky since time immemorial (The Book of The Damned...Lo! New Lands).

We may use Occam's Razor to advantage here; a simple explanation is at hand for all these mysteries. There is no need to multiply the theories and explanations to a point of inanity, simply because there are rigid orthodoxies or because the thoughts of extraterrestrials within our solar system is threatening or frightening. The sheer inanity and stupidity of proliferating theories to avoid the truth is shown most of all in the UFO experience, but also in such matters as Lunar Transient Phenomena, where NASA has developed (with its scientific advisers) seven hypotheses to explain them, not one of which makes sense as a cause of » several phenomena over time. So, when Occam's Razor does not suit their purpose, it is quickly overlooked as a guide.

The Moon is occupied—that, like the facts that Earth revolves around the sun and the sun is a mediocre star on the fringe cf the galaxy, is true, and there is nothing we can do right now to change it. It is time we stopped behaving like primitives, and it is time for our professionals to begin living up to their trust (we paid for a good portion of their graduate educations) and begin leading instead of confusing us.

7. *While there is scant evidence of outright hostility, it appears from the body of reliable data that one or more of! the races on the Moon regards us with disdain and values human life cheaply.*

If hostility were part of the game plan, we'd have experienced it overtly and definitely by now. Races capable of moving between star systems (or time frames or dimensions—who knows?) and existing on the Moon must also be capable of wiping us out at will.

It is probably this (understandably) which panics the military.

But beyond what appear to be accidents (e.g., Captain Mantell's plane crash while chasing a huge UFO; see Scientific Study of Unidentified Flying Objects [Bantam, 1968], pages 504-505), isolated incidents such as serious burns from a UFO (e.g., the fort in South America reported by Coral and Jim Lorenzen in UFO: The Whole Stoi-y [Signet, 1969], and the Bermuda Triangle cases involving possible kidnappings and scattered reports which are difficult to get. a handle on, there is no body of data which would lead one unequivocally to conclude that They plan something nefarious.

On the contrary, hypothesis No. 2 assumes that one of the occupants' chief missions is mining (and it may be first in priority), a mission which involves the persons of Earth only indirectly. (We would be directly involved, of course, if at any time or in any way we challenged their right to carry out that mission. Any volunteers?)

But reliable records indicate that the extraterrestrials for the most part treat us as we might treat chickens in a barnyard: We avoid hurting them if we can, but don't lose sleep when we do. Sometimes They show disdain, curiosity, interest—hut rarely friendliness or compassion (See the Lorenzens' book, Encounters With UFO Occupants).

In the meantime, They are content to do Their work and mix it up with curiosity tours, zoology, botany, and stealing whatever suits Their needs and fancy.

8. *The occupants of the Moon shifted long ago in Their history from biological to mechanical bodies, although control may still be with biological brains; and biological entities may be with Them to fulfill certain roles.*

The shift to mechanical bodies, keeping the brain and perhaps certain basic nerve centers, means increasing life span several hundred percent. It means greater efficiency, greater strength, doing away with a horde of physical illnesses and problems of aging. It does not have to mean doing away with sensual pleasure; that level of technology could meet, all needs and desires through the knowledge of stimulation of parts of the brain and nervous system, with pleasurable sensual results. (Too, the shift to mechanical bodies may take place only after the biological body has had its full complement of stimuli.)

The chances of our ever confronting an extraterrestrial group which has also just hit the electromagnetic age are near the vanishing point. If They negotiate space or time or dimensions. They have been technologically advanced for thousands or millions of years. If the potential for some technologies in the center of the galaxy is several million years, then the law of averages indicates that any particular race would more likely be in a "science-sophistication" period well along the spectrum.

The shift to partial or total body mechanization can be counted on as a function of advanced technologies. This is not as sweeping a generalization as it sounds. Note that I used the word "partial." We are just about ready on Earth to provide mechanical hearts—a first step. We know how to make artificial limbs which respond to the wearer's nerve impulses. Soon artificial kidneys will function inside people. What next?

Some time ago I was puzzling over what the occupants f of the Moon might really want, what They are doing. The [far-out (and frightening) thought came to me that extra-terrestrials who were hominoids—that is, similar to us be- j cause we came from the same seed in the universe—might j be perpetuating themselves by using our bodies or parts of your bodies when theirs wear out. It could explain the Bermuda Triangle, and the fact that thousands of people in the world are missing every year and are never seen again.

Where is it written that technological competence equals our moral standards?

But if a shift is desirable, a well-designed, perfected mechanical heart would be superior to one of our short-range models. Let's quote a man who is a physicist, engineer, and astronomer, and a Fellow of the Royal Society of Medicine: C. Maxwell Cade, the author of Other Worlds than Ours (Taplinger Publishing Co., New York, 1967):

"*We are clearly a long way yet from having complete technological control of our environment, but at the present rate of progress it should come within a few hundred years. After that, unless we destroy ourselves in some stupid fratricidal war, we must presume that there is a relatively long period during which civilization will maintain itself at the level of superior technological mastery of environment—either in the form of a society of Great Brains, or of a biological society which uses machines, including superior mechanical intelligences, to do all its work for it.*

If we make the reasonable assumption that some roughly similar time scale is involved in the development of intelligence upon other worlds, we see that the chance is only one in tens of millions of meeting beings at our own level—that is to say, in the process of rapid transition from the long ages of no technology to the ages of superior technology.

We see then, that when we are able to undertake interstellar exploration, whether it be in manned spacecraft or by means of automatic probes, the odds are enormous that the beings we find will be either little better than animals, or superior intelligences with scientific and engineering skills beyond our comprehension. This is why it is important to give thought to the probability of encountering mechanical intelligences ... to races at the necessary level of advanced technology there would seemingly be incalculable advantages in making the change from biological to mechanical bodies at the earlier opportunity. [Italics added. Failure to grasp the italicized portion of Cade's statement leads some observers and scientists to retreat to orthodox views on the Moon simply because what they see is beyond their comprehension. Too many,perhaps, expect that sentient life based there would be revealed through Earth-type buildings, superhighways, etc.]"

There is more than theoretical strength behind this hypothesis; descriptions of UFO occupants and their behavior lend support. "Slitlike mouths which did not move as they spoke," "Stiff gait with jerky movements," "Voice which seemed to come from the chest and sounded metallic" are some of the descriptions given by highly credible witnesses when talking about one particular kind of occupants. "He moved like a mechanical wind-up toy," stated a woman in Erie, Pennsylvania, describing a UFO occupant seen by others in the vicinity as well (reported by John A. Keel in Strange Creatures from Time and Space, page 162).

Much of the body of data on creatures seen in and around UFOs (a very large and reliable body of data) is consistent with this hypothesis. For a more detailed look at automated behavior, read the testimony given under hypnosis by Betty and Barney Hill, in Fuller's Interrupted Journey (Dial Press, 1966); and the comprehensive collection of reports of extraterrestrial contact by the Lorenzens, Encounters With UFO Occupants, Berkley, 1976.

9. *The prime reason for the United States' launching an expensive Moon program (and sending spacecraft to Mars and beyond) was the recognition at official levels that the Moon (and perhaps Mars) is occupied by intelligent extraterrestrials who have a mission which does not include dialogue with us and may even be inimical to our long-range welfare.*

Corollary (a): Lack of knowledge as to Their aims has led to the placing of a security clamp on the truth about the Moon.

Corollary (b): Now that Their presence on the Moon has been confirmed, our prime goal is to learn whether They come from within the solar system (e.g., Mars, a moon of Jupiter, Venus) or from another star system.

So you believe we poured billions into the Moon program just because it "was there"? Just to satisfy some research scientists who must describe, measure? Just because the public clamored for exploration of it? (Needless to say, there was no public clamor for exploring the Moon. It is the clearest example of how we live not in a democracy but in something which might be called an autocratic technocracy.)

There are places on this Earth which cry out for expensive research programs and which could return far more to us in terms of benefits to mankind than can any Moon probe. The sea is a good example. We know little about the deep troughs; we've not scratched the surface in gaining knowledge on the possibility that the sea can feed the hordes of people we're breeding; we have only small inklings as to the remains of ancient cities known to have been where the bottom of the Atlantic is now. (See the bibliography in Berlitz's Bermuda Triangle.)

Yet we chose the Moon. For good reasons. We put enough billions into it to pull all the major cities of America out of debt, and then some. And after the successful Ranger and Surveyor and Orbiter and Apollo flights, we] dropped manned lunar exploration like a hot potato.

Less than twenty percent of the data resulting from these probes has been studied.

Less than two percent has been reported on.

Did we pay $27 billion to learn that a rock from highland breccia is almost 4.1 billion years old?

Did we lose three good men to a launching accident to learn that you won't, after all (as one astronomer said you would), sink into a thousand feet of soft dust on the Moon? „

If the answer to these questions is "No," then there must be something which is different today about the Moon in relation to us—different than it was in the early sixties.

That difference is that we have seen the construction and the mechanical rigs and the craters being sprayed and the manufactured devices. Close up. We have seen the changes and the gas vented out of the stacks and the dust getting kicked up, and we now know They are there—living and working and God knows what else right under our noses.

Question: How do you deal with uncommunicative extraterrestrials who can stop your vehicle dead and can freeze you in your tracks and can chew up a mountain ridge with two-mile-long rigs?

Answer: Very carefully.

Question; What do you do after you've seen Them at close range and have a gut feeling They'll go away only when They have finished what They are doing?

Answer: You go away on little cat feet, and tell the world you're finished with manned landings for the foreseeable future.

And if you are in the inner circles of intelligence—the National Security Council or the Forty Committee—you crinkle your eyes and puff on your pipe and say there is no need for the public to know. No need at all. What good would it do them? What would they do with the knowledge? Most of them care more about the latest news about Jackie, or the price of gasoline. Would telling the truth to this public shake its confidence in religion, the dollar, law and order? Might it give rise to a new and more dangerous breed of crackpot than the UFO engendered? Would it get in the way of defense strategy?

The scientists are easily persuaded. If a few of their leaders are taken into confidence, they then can handle the others. They showed their ability to be discreet during the enormous Manhattan Project in the early forties. They have shown it all down through the years of the cold war, when the lion's share of research in many fields was related to the military. If you are in the club, you can't afford to be a fink.

A prime reason for security is simply that the country which first learns the secrets of the advanced technology evidenced by the extraterrestrials will control the world. How do you create an electromagnetic force which stops an ignition system cold? (Learn that and you can immobilize an army.) How do you make a craft go many thousands of miles an hour without rocketry or other visible propulsion? (Learn that and what good are your enemy's nuclear-bomb-bearing planes and intercontinental ballistic missiles?) If the Russians learn it first, will they use it to control the non-Communist world? If the Americans do, what will they do with it?

I confess that this cold-war need for security (artificially enhanced by the very existence of both the CIA and the KGB) is the one factor dissuading me from my initial belief that, behind the scenes, the United States and Russia were really cooperating in space. I could not bring myself to believe that both countries would rip off their citizens to the outrageous extent of mountain separate and duplicate space programs. Yet, notwithstanding the blatant competition between the two political-economic systems, I will not be too surprised if it proves true that cooperation has existed from the beginning. The effects of having extraterrestrials (whose aims are not crystal clear) ensconced on our Moon are incalculable, and could transcend our mundane differences. ^

There are hints which perspicacious people will not ignore. For example, the Apollo 17 report contains references to the results of various Russian lunar probes (see the Introduction), which means that the Russians have actually been turning over to us their data—and, obviously, we must have been reciprocating. And a careful review of total United States and Russian space shots seems to indicate that a parceling out of responsibility has existed from the start: "Your turn to curtsey, my turn to bow." Although both NASA and the Russian Embassy failed to respond to my request for a clear identification of the purpose for each Russian moon shot, Dr. Wittcomb and I put together fragments from here and there (aided by the McGrow Hill Encyclopedia of Space) and could not find one single example of definite duplication between the payloads of the two countries' moon probes. This division of responsibilities is even more apparent in the Venus, Mars, and other non- moon probes.

This has been one person's attempt to communicate what he sees, feels, and thinks about the Moon as it really is. But it is only the merest introduction. If you wish to go further, the Bibliography may be helpful along with selected .photographs of the Moon.

Above all, this book is not meant to convince anyon

change anyone's mind, merely by one's reading it. If some are stimulated to do hard but fascinating work with the photos, I will feel that the book has created change. Few scientists will read it anyway, and none will readjust his/her views; they have already been told what to think, and that's that.

Perhaps the most fascinating quotation I came across during work on this book is the one preceding the Introduction to the Apollo 17 Preliminary Science Report: "There is nothing more difficult to take in hand, or perilous to conduct, or more uncertain in its success, than to take the lead in the introduction of a new order of things." What makes it fascinating? The quotation's author: Niccolo Machiavelli. He was a Haldemanlike character to royalty in sixteenth-century Italy. He wrote The Prince. The book, a classic studied in most basic university courses on government today, is a practical guide to running a government. It is so practical that the term "Machiavellian" has come to mean leadership characterized by cunning, duplicity, bad faith. Any deception of the populace, including twisted information, is justified so long as it suits the needs and fancies of those in power.

Niccolo Machiavelli also said the following (original sixteenth-century translation English retained):

"And therefore a wise Prince cannot, nor ought not to keep his faith given, when the observance thereof turns to disadvantage, and the occasions that mads his promise, are past. . . .Let a Prince therefore take the surest courses he can to maintain his life and State: the means shall always be thought honorable, and commended by every one: for the vulgar is overtaken with the appearance and event of a thing: and for the most part of people, they are but the vulgar: the others that are but few, take place where the vulgar have no subsistence."

Quoting Machiavelli to lead off the 17th Apollo probe reports is, in view of what the American people are not being told about the Moon, most appropriate.

And Sam Wittcomb read my manuscript in draft and then sat staring into the black night. When he spoke, it was in a hushed voice. I'd never heard him like that before. "They brought scientists together from many countries back in the Spring of 1975. The meeting was in England. They wanted to talk on the quiet about extraterrestrials and what they're tip to. A lot of people at the top are scared." A cold spot formed in the small of my back. Sam turned to me. "They invited a physicist from Colorado, a man named Joachim Kuetner, who'd worked on the Moon program and knows what's up there. He could tell them about it first-hand. About the frenetic building and digging going on, the spraying of craters and carving up of crater rims and ridges. I don't know exactly what they talked about. But you can bet they know now that it's not Earthpeople's Moon anymore—if it ever was. It belongs to Them."

-- FIN --

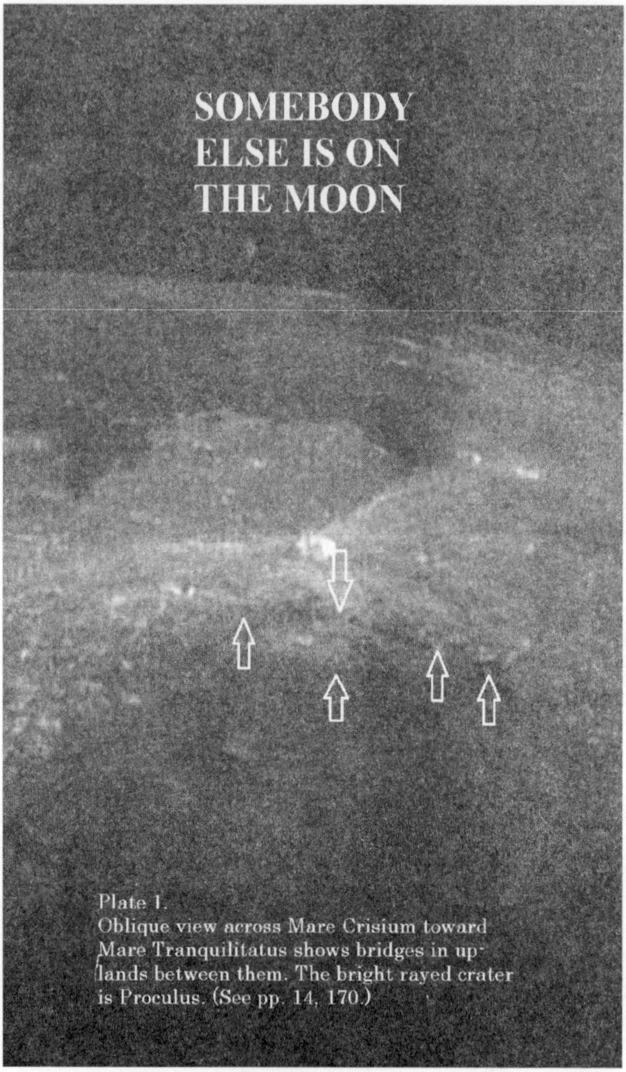

Plate 1

AS16-121-19438

Mare Crisium

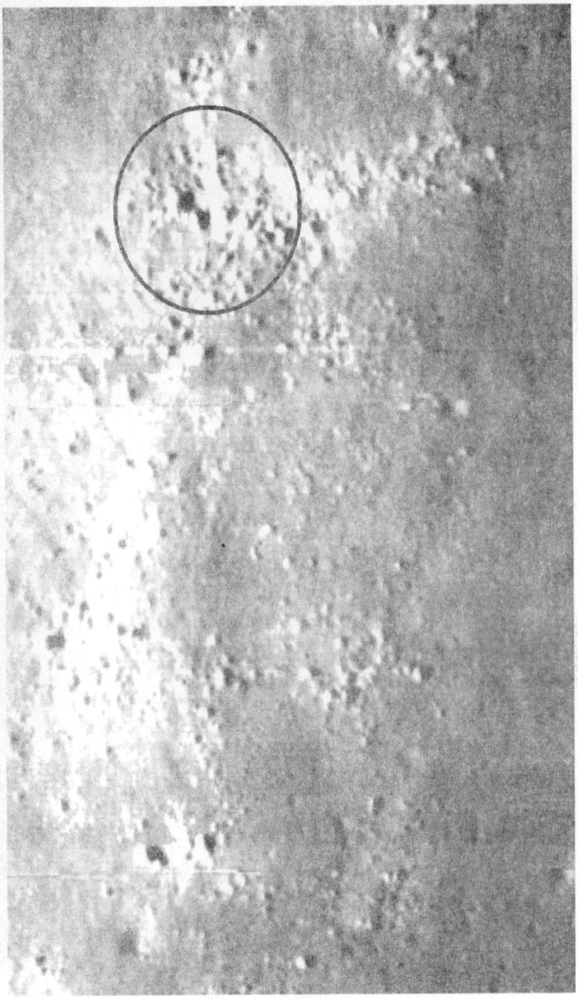

Plate 2
66-H-1612 (LO-II-042-H2)
Manufactured objects and vehicle are visible in Mare Tranquillitatus. (See pp. 24, 100-101.)

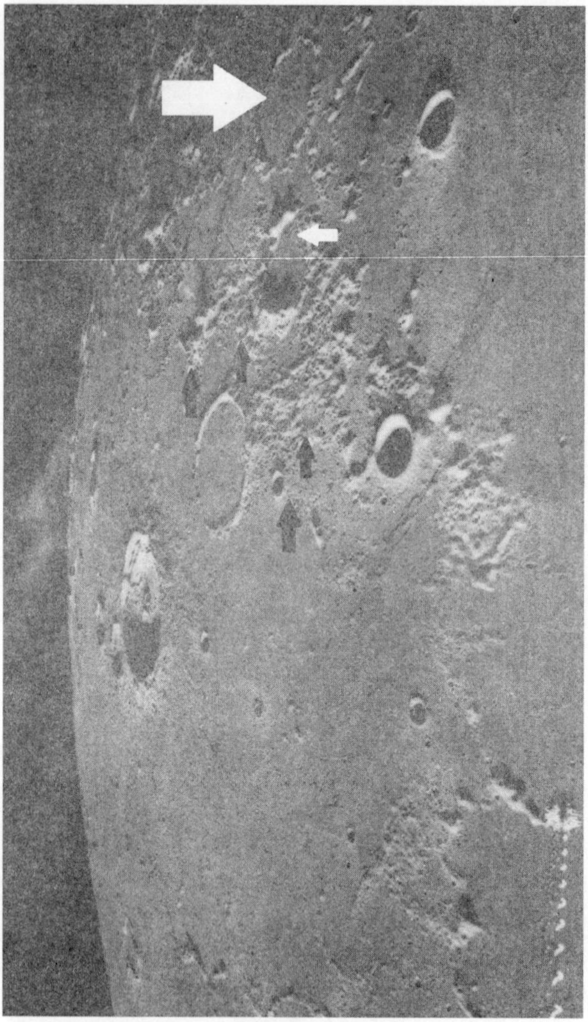

Plate 3.
72-H-1367 (AS16M-2493) See also LO-IV-125-H2
Machinery and stitches are indicated in the Bullialdus-Lubinicky area. Large white arrow indicates
Lubinicky E crater. (See pp. 42, 136, 167.)

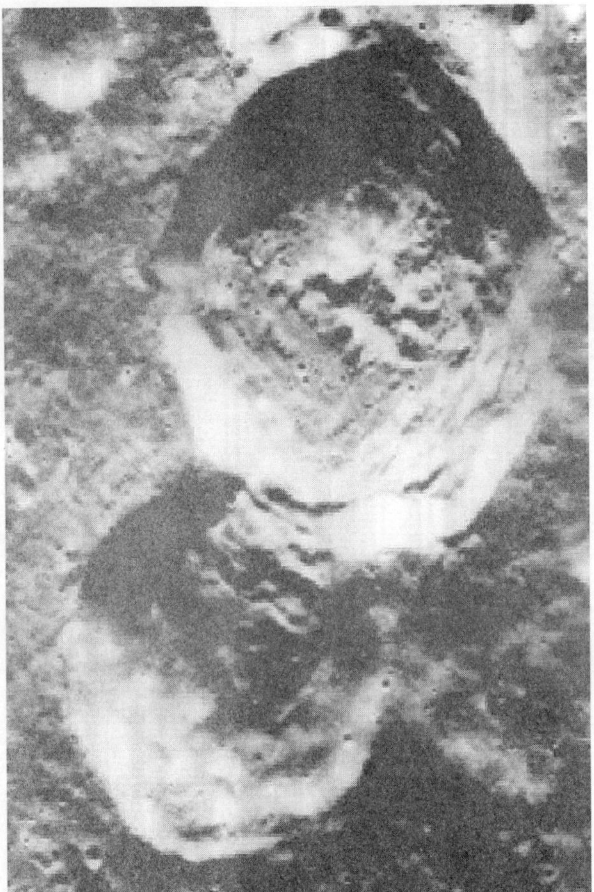

Plate 4

66-H-1293 (LO-I-1136-H3)

This farside shot was taken from Lunar Orbiter 1 and shows a super rig at approximately two o'clock at the base of the walls of the octagonal crater.

(See pp. 49, 50,51.)

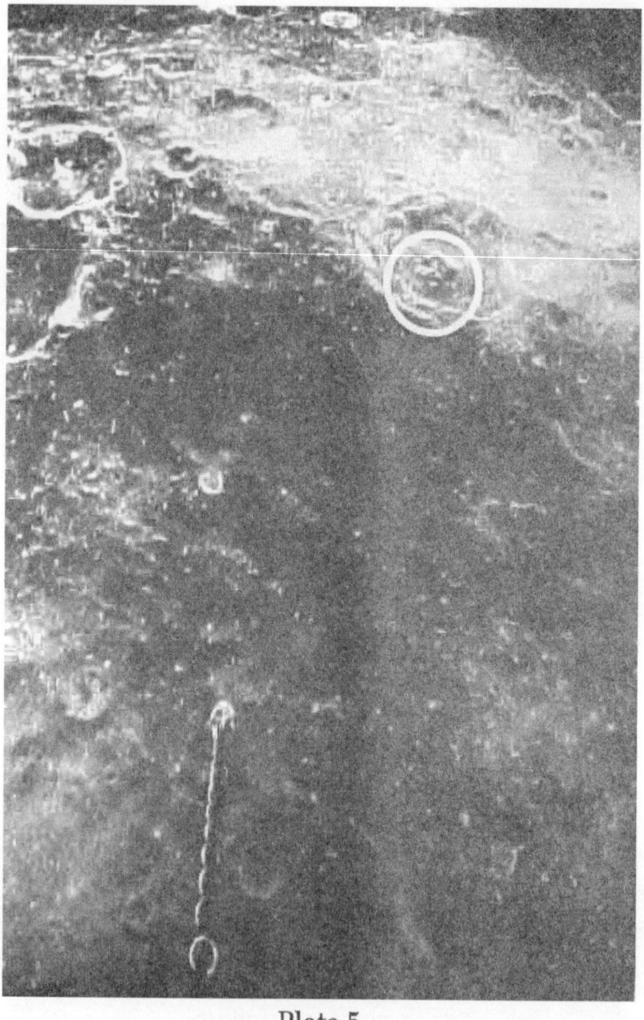

Plate 5

72-H-1109 (LO number cannot be cross-referenced at this time.) T-scoop is indicated cutting away the central mountain of the crater in this area immediately east of Mare Smythii. (See pp. 53, 58-59.)

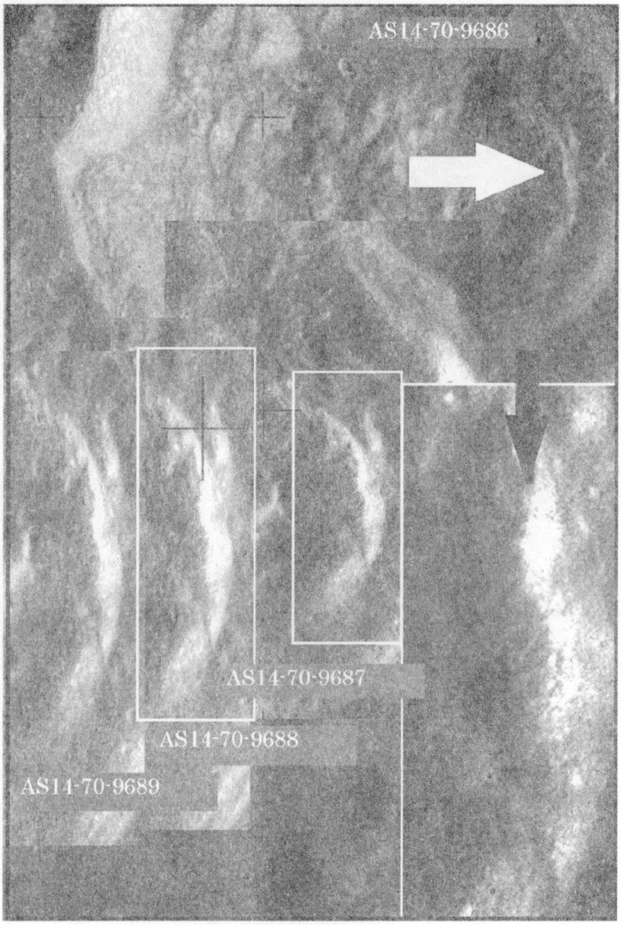

Plate-6

71-H-781 (AS14-70-9686--89)

Notice the super rig on the crater terrace photographed by the Apollo 14. (See pp. 54.)

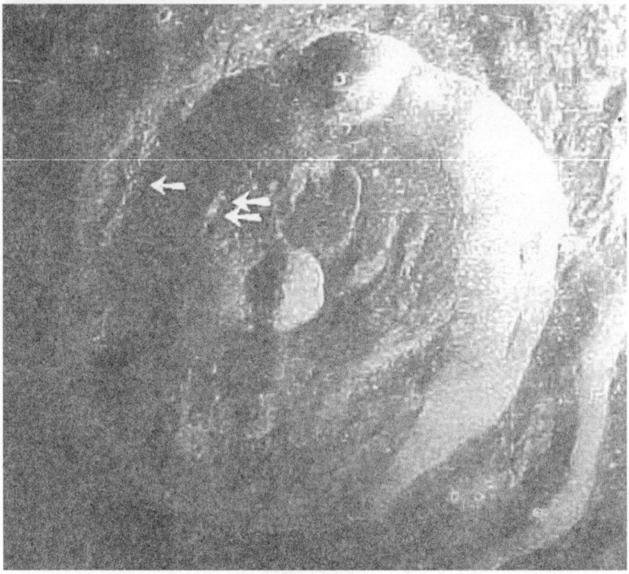

Plate-7
(69-H-25)
(LO number cannot be cross-referenced from
the HQ NASA number at this time.)
Two X-drones on crater floor and one on crater ridge
are
enlarging this farside crater by already obvious
spiral cuts.
(See pp. 56-57.)

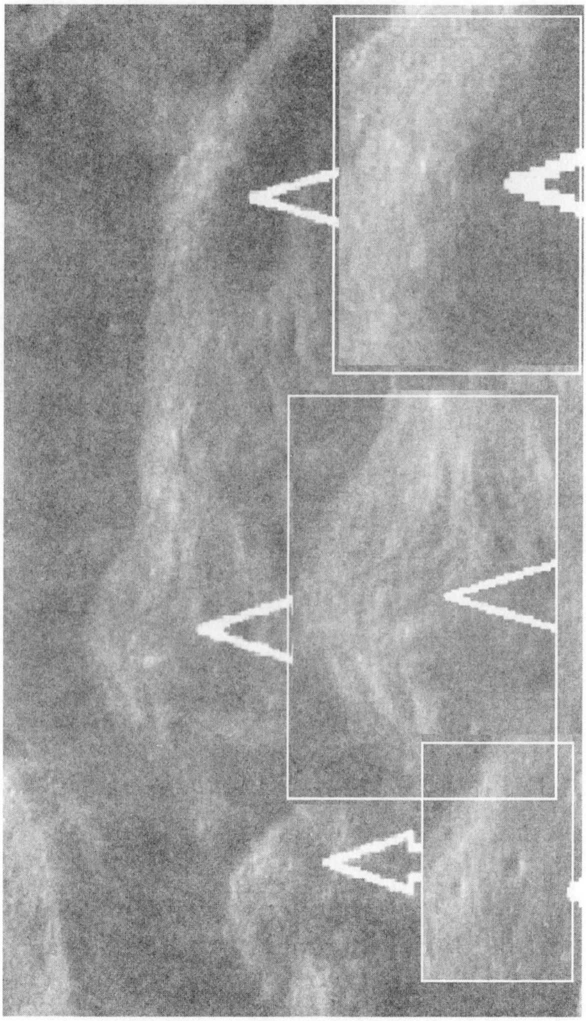

Plate-8a
72-H-837 (Similar to AS16-P-5000)
X-drones are raising dust on the rim of King Crater.
(See pp. 57, 69-70.)

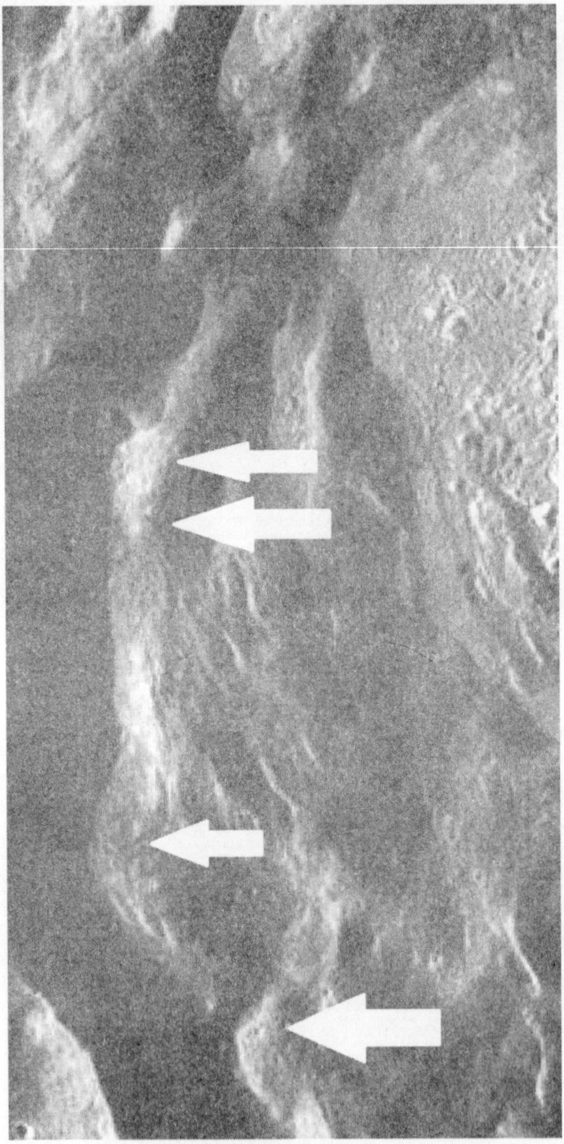

Leonard's PLATE-8
(AS16-P-5000)

Plate-9

69-H-1206 (LO-V-125-H2)

Domes are visible at the center top, construction and stitches are squared in the left; a crater covering at the right and tracks at the left are indicated by arrows, and a large screw is enclosed in a rectangle, all on the floor of Tycho.

(See pp. 61, 124.)

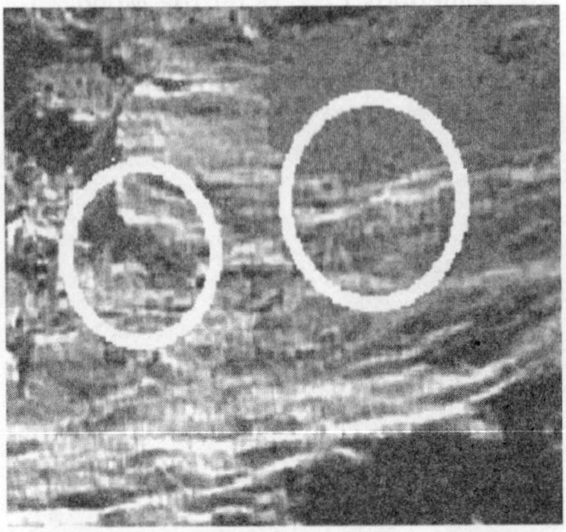

Plate 10 (A)

72-H-834--836 (AS16-120-19263--19267)

Notice the indicated cannon-shaped object which casts a shadow, and a spraying crater in the highlands between King Crater and an unnamed ponding effect crater.

(See pp. 63, 74-75, 80.)

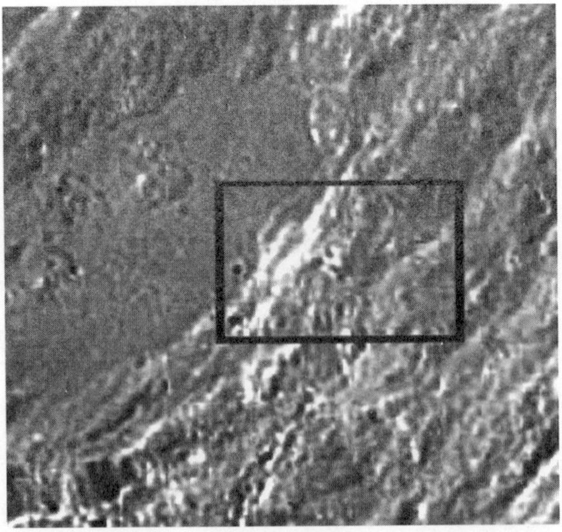

Plate 10 (B)

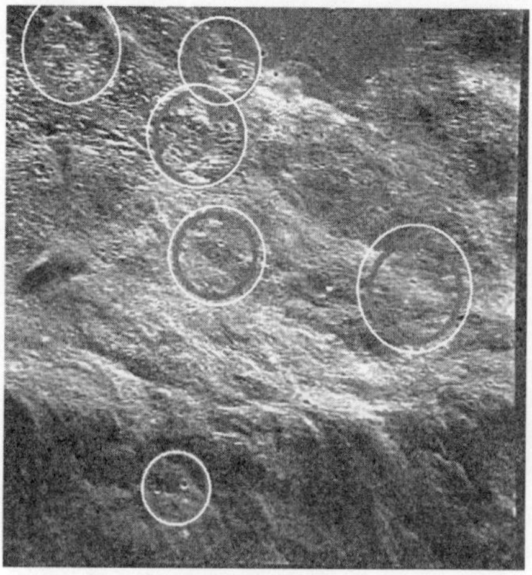

Plate 10 (C)
Another view of Leonard's King Crater area objects.

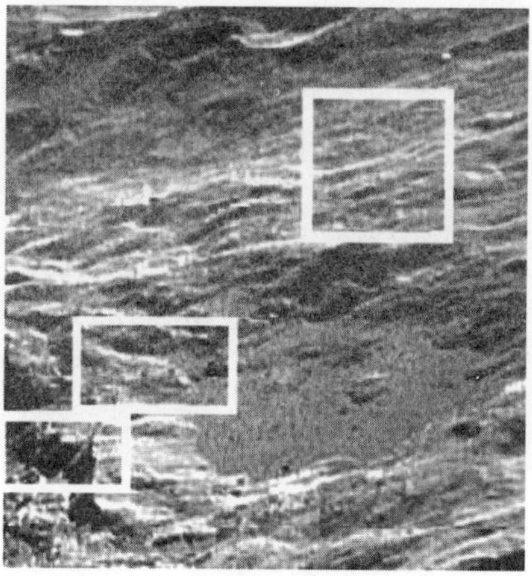

Plate 11
72-H-836 (AS16-120-19226)
A small spraying crater is located in the highlands of the King Crater area. (See pp. 63, 75.)

Plate 12

72-H-839 (AS16-120-19228)

Arrows indicate several small craters in the process of being worked with marking crosses on their lips and spraying drones inside. Also notice X-drones and puff-like orbs circled in this shot of area near King Crater. (See pp. 63, 67, 74-75, 76, 77, 80,81, 183.)

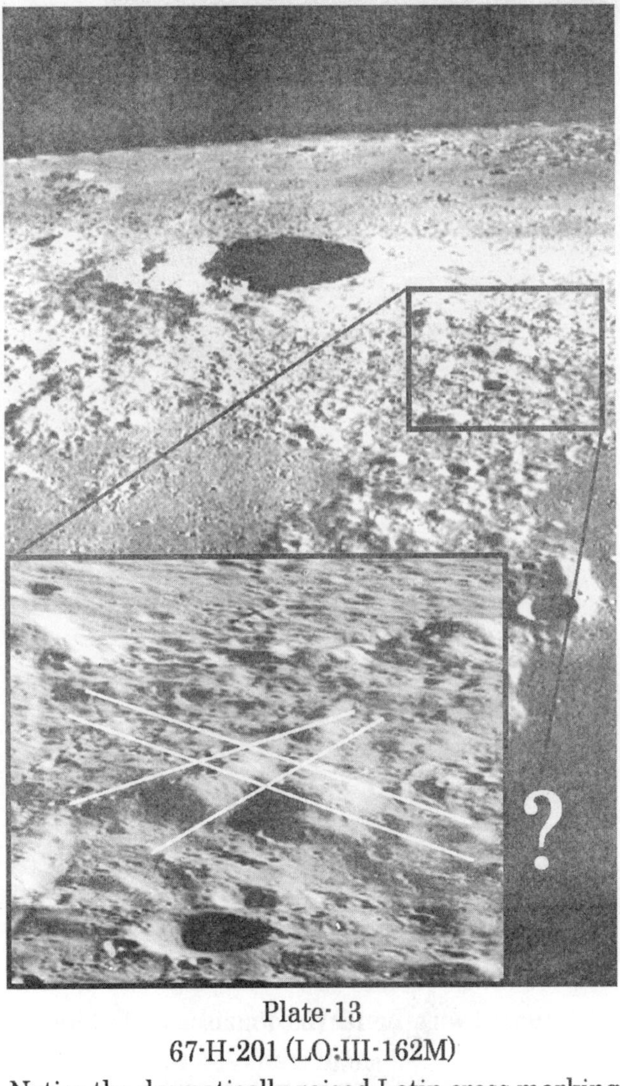

Plate-13
67-H-201 (LO:III-162M)
Notice the dramatically raised Latin cross marking indicated near Crater Kepler.
(See pp. 65-66.)

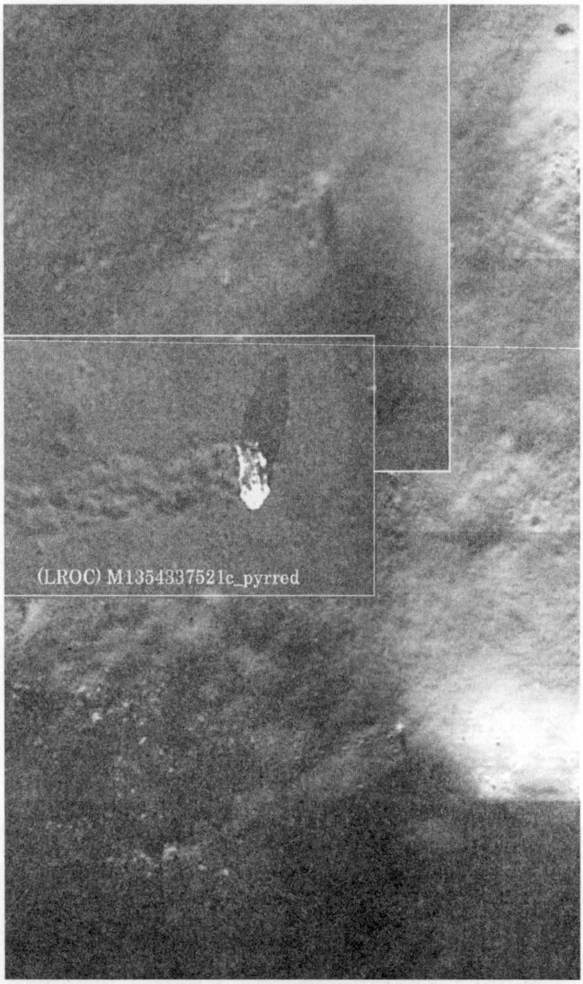

Plate-14

67-H-1135 (LO-V-168-H2)

Compared with Lunar Reconnaissance Orbiter Camera photo.

(LROC) M1354337521c_pyrred

Two "rolling" objects on the floor of Vitello Crater. Note that the smaller object "rolled" up, out of the crater. (See pp. 96.)

Plate-15

67-H-758 (LO-II-62-H3)

Note the similarity of form in this group of objects with two bump appendages in a cratered upland basin photographed by Lunar Orbiter II.

(See pp. 96.)

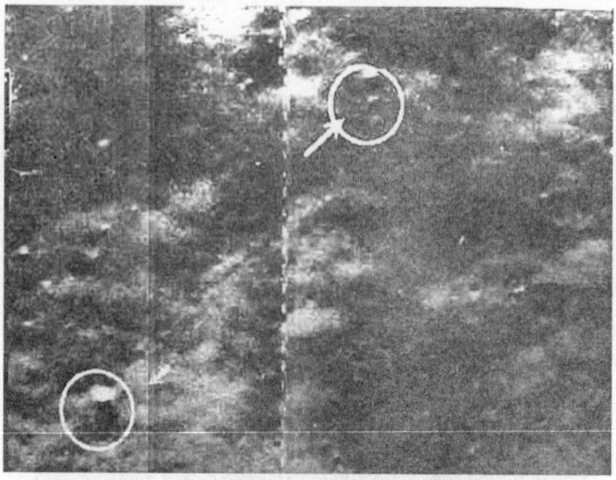

Plate-16

67-H-510

(Leonard's photo. LO and Apollo shots of Crater Sabine D could not be found.)

Two objects are indicated which have tracks from "rolling" in opposite directions in Crater Sabine D. (See pp. 100.)

Plate-17

67-H-327

Vehicle rests inside anomalous rayed crater in Oceanus Procellarum. Note that rays especially originate from corners of polygon. (See pp. 102.)

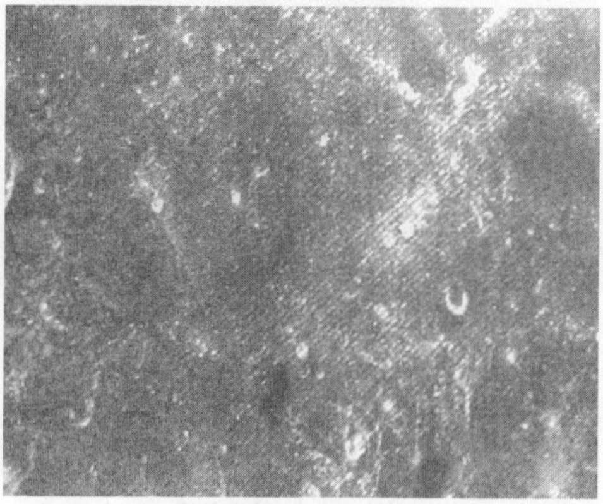

Plate-18
(Leonard's photo)

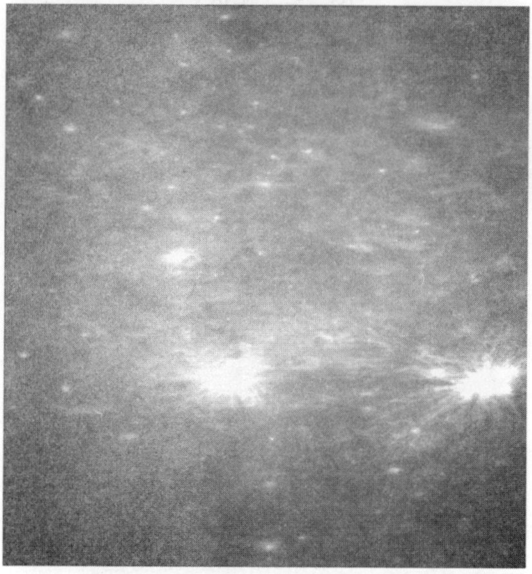

Better example of rayed craters

Plate-19

67-H-1179

Coverings with glyph and manufactured object are indicated in Crater Tycho. (See pp. 120, 127.)

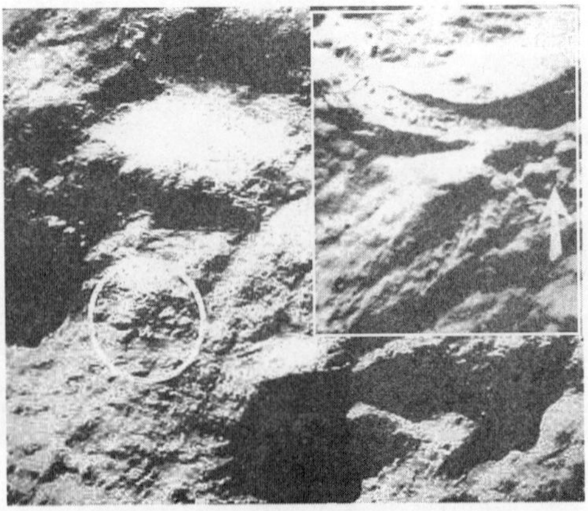

Plate-20

Power source plate with knobs and cord (right), and constructions and gas spray (left), in Tycho.

(See pp. 123, 127, 129.)

Plate-21

67-H-187 (LO-II-62-M and H3, II-61-H3)

[See also LROC m159847595RC_pyr]

Shadow of obelisk indicates a horizontal bar on top in photograph from Lunar Orbiter III.

(See pp. 168.)

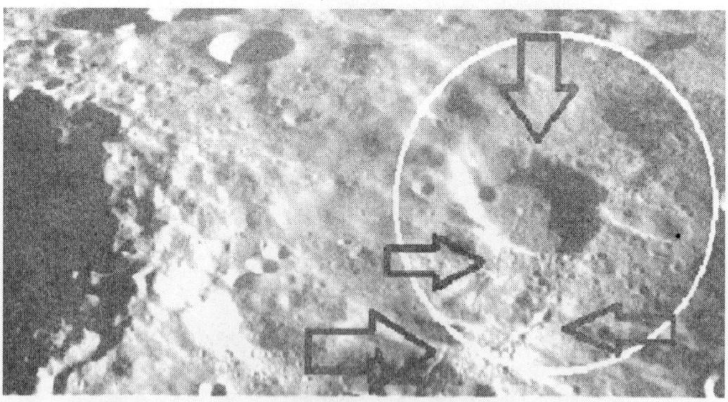

Plate-22

69-H-8 (AS8-13-2244)

Tread marks on rim and rope ladder or tread extending from rim to floor are visible on this farside crater photographed by Apollo 8.

(See p.174.)

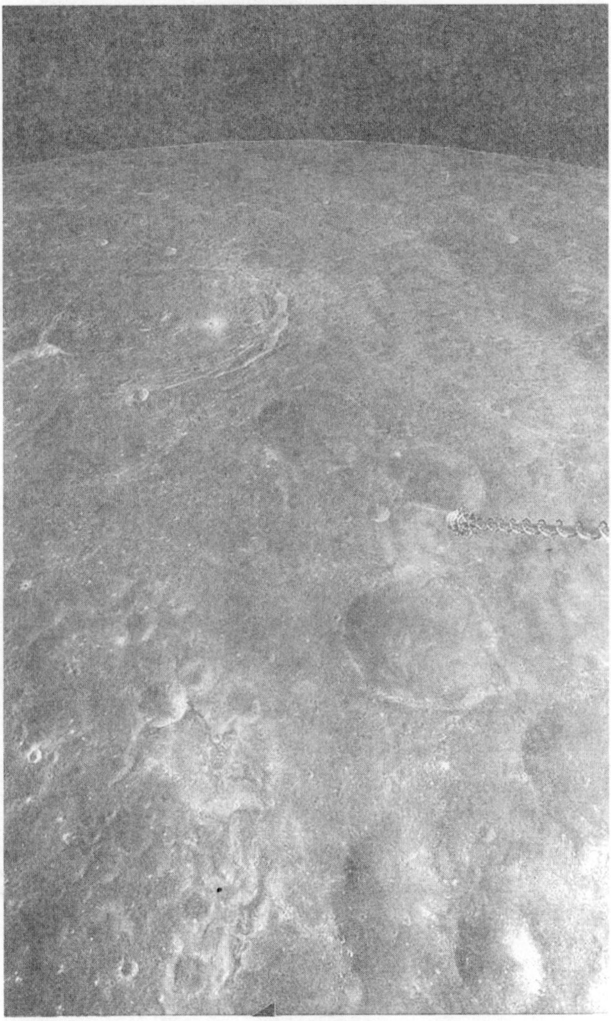

Plate-23

72-H-1113 (AS16-M-0758)

Unexplained white light, which may be pure energy, is flowing over the rim of Lobachavsky Crater. (See pp.

175-176.)

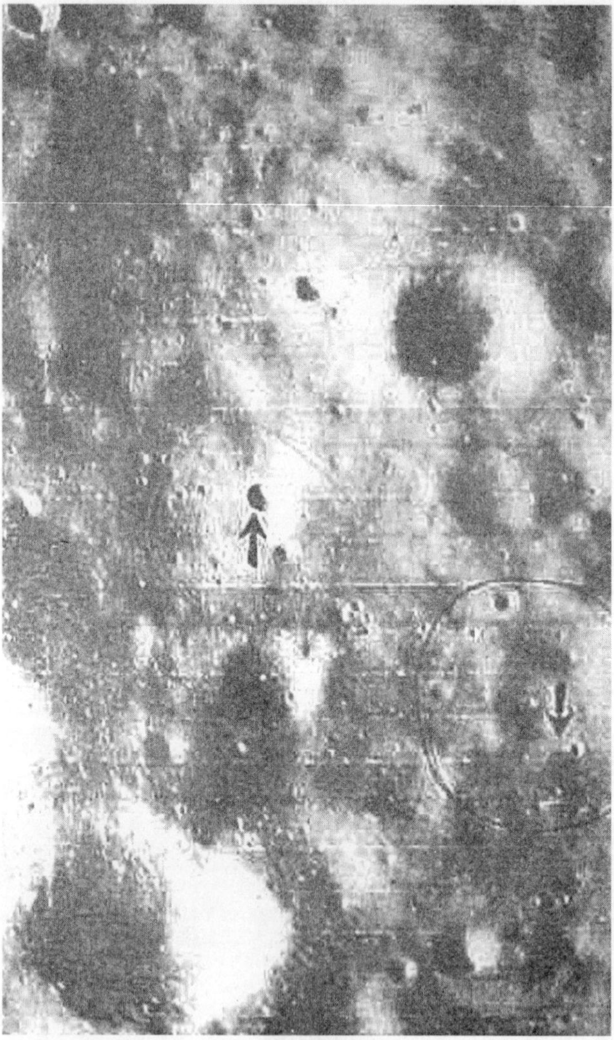

Plate-24

Control wheels extending into two craterlets reflect sunlight in the Fra Mauro area.

(See pp. 176, 179.)

Plate-25

67-H-304 (Surveyor-III ?)

A sharply defined, machine-tooled object is indicated in area south of Maskelyne F. (See p. 177.)

Plate-26

70-H-1629

Anomalous crater being covered over near top and two small craters containing activity are indicated in Fra Mauro area. (See p. 178.)

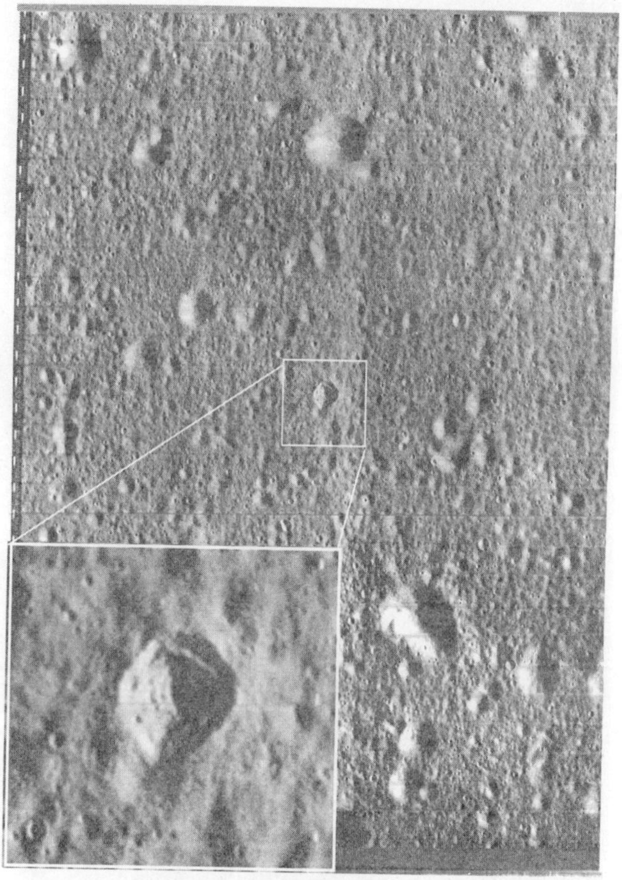

Plate-27
67-H-41 (LO-II-182-H1)
Control wheels visible in sharply defined crater at center
of photo of a mare southeast of Crater Kepler.
(See p. 179.)

Plate-28

67-H-266 (LO-III-194-H2)

Diamond opening is visible in clearly defined anomalous crater in lower photo area of Surveyor-I landing site. (See p. 180.)

Plate-29

67-H-935 (LO-IV-187-H2)

Construction area reflects sunlight at right upper edge of photograph of area of Mare Orientale, Mar Veris, Rook Mountains. (See pp. 181, 186-87.)

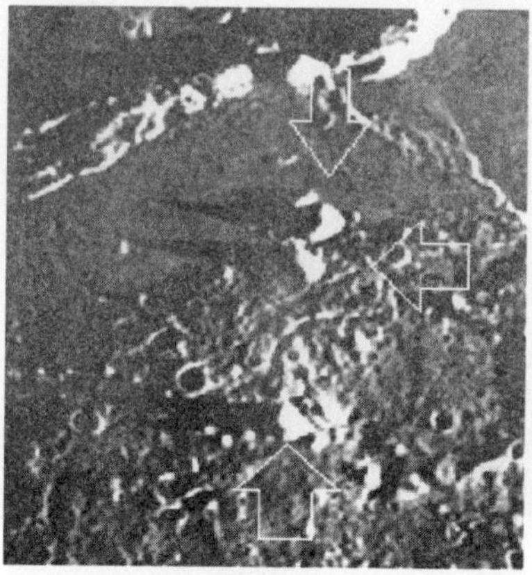

Plate-30

71-H-1300, 1765

Platform with dome casts narrow triangular shadow above sensor probe at right: Herodotus mountain range and Oceanus Procellarum. (See p. 182.)

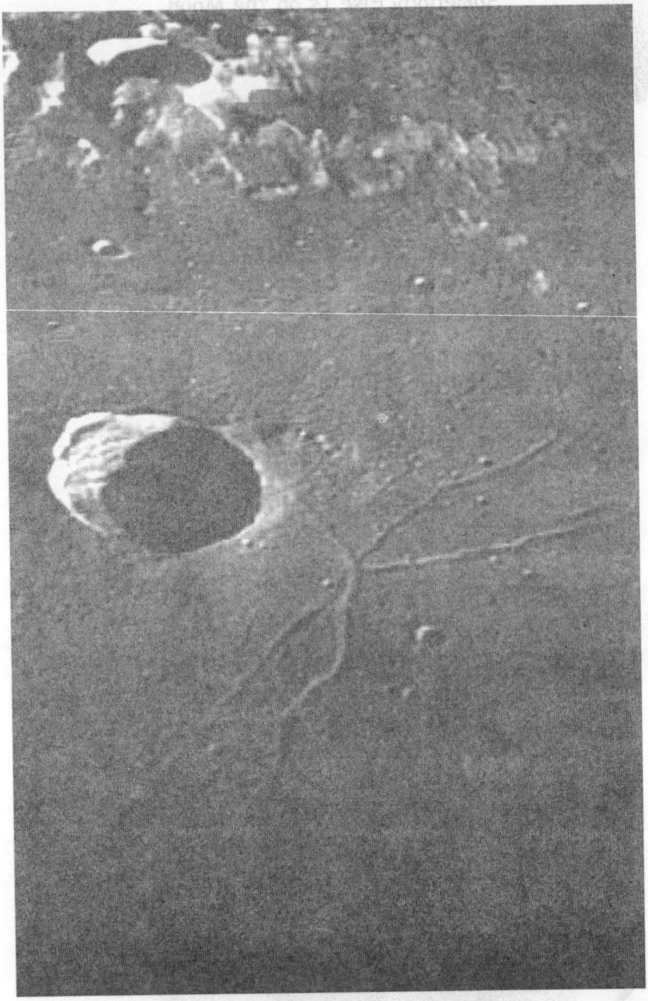

Plate-31

69-H-737 (AS10-32-4819)

Regularly parallel ribbing on surface is indicated in area of Triesnecker Crater. (See pp. 182-83.)

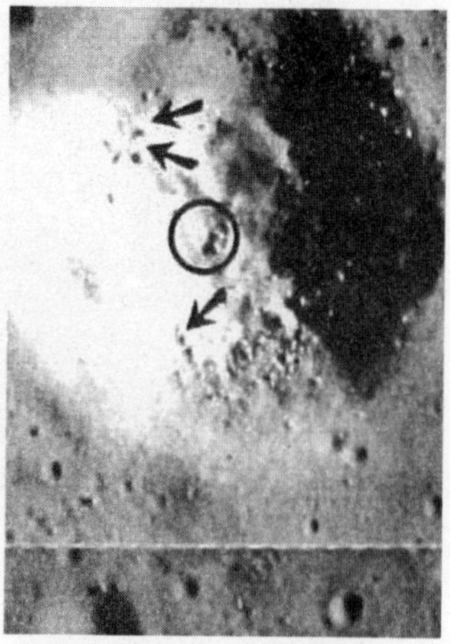

Plate-32 66-H-1611

Familiar two bump objects and a T-bar plumbing are indicated in crater in western Mare Tranquillitatus. (See p. 185.)

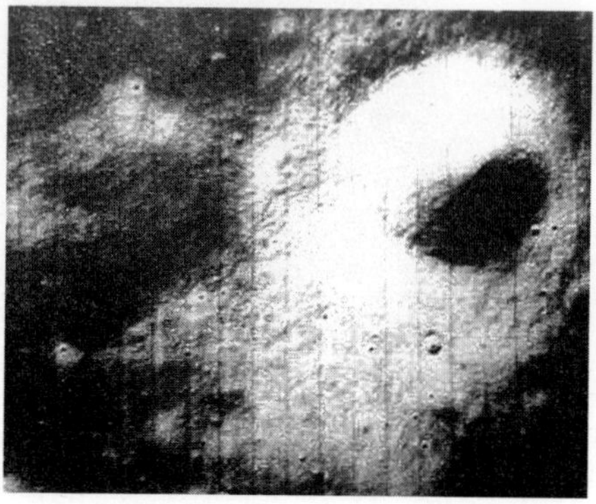

Plate 33 67-H-318

Manufactured artifact clearly visible on floor of crater near center right in Oceanus Procellarum. (See pp. 185, 186.)

Plate-34

67-H-307

Right-angled pipe is located in craterlet in southern Mare Tranquillitatus. (See p. 185.)

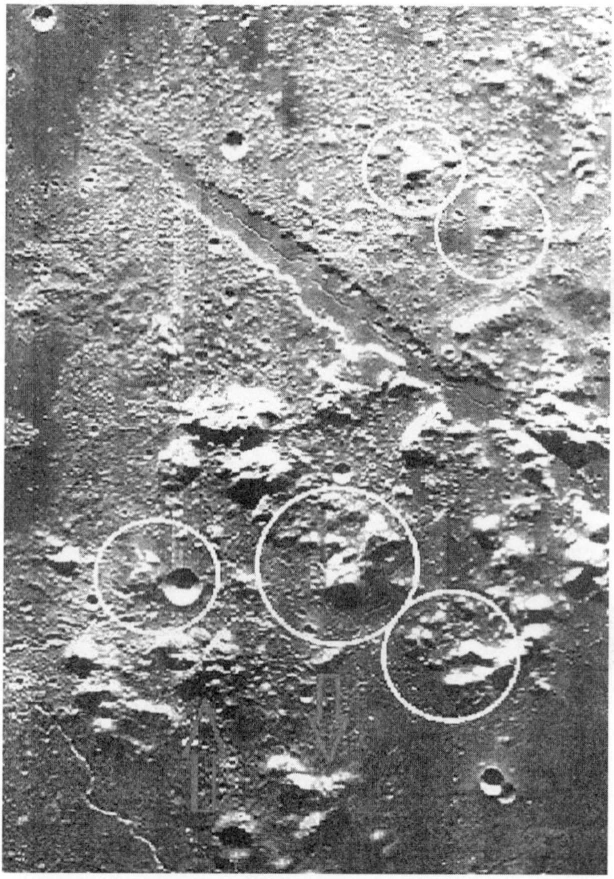

Plate-35
67-H-897, 1400, 1409 (LO-IV-115-H3)
Some of the many constructions are located in the Alpine Valley. (See pp. 187, 188-90.)

APPENDIX - 1

Leonard's NASA photo numbers, phenomena, and lunar locations - Cross-referenced to Johnson Space Center LO Numbers:

66-H-1293 lunar far side octagonal crater L. Orbiter I
= LO-I-1136-H3

66-H-1611 Western Mare Tranquillitatis

66-H-1612 South-eastern Mare Tranquillitatis
= LO-II-42-H1-3?

67-H-41 (plate-27) Mare southeast of crater Kepler
= LO-II-182-H1

67-H-187 (plate-28) Lunar Orbiter III
= LO-III-012-H1

67-H-201 Crater Kepler in Oceanus crater
= LO-III-162-M and "H1"

67-H-266 anomalous crater Surveyor I landing site

67-H-304 South of Maskelyne F

67-H-318 Oceanus Procellarum

67-H-307 West of Rima Maskelyne in Southern Mare Tranquillitatis

67-H-327 crater in Oceanus Procellarum

67-H-510 Crater Sabine D

67-H-758 Cratered upland basin taken Lunar Orbiter II
= LO-II-62-H3 and "M"

67-H-897 Northeast of Mare Imbrium near Alpine Valley
= LO-IV-115-H3

67-H-935 Mare Orientale. Mare Veris and Rook Mountains
= LO-IV-187-H2

67-H-1135 Crater Vitello with Boulder Track
= LO-V-168-H2

67-H-1179 Tycho crater Tycho

67-H-1206 Tycho Crater

67-H-1400

67-H-1409

67-H-1651 Crater Tycho and northern highlands

67-H-8 lunar far side taken from Apollo 8
= AS8-13-2244

69-H-25 unnamed far side crater

69-H-28 Crater Humboldt and Southern Sea surrounding craters

69-H-737 Triesnecker crater

69-H-1206 Tycho Floor
= LO-IV-125-M

70-H-1629 Fra Mauro area

70-H-1630 Fra Mauro area

70-H-781 Taken by Apollo 14

70-H-1300

70-H-1765 Oceanus Procellarum and Herodotus

70-H-834 North-western half of King Crater
= AS16-120-19263--19267

72-H-835 Mare Crisium, Mare Tranquillitatis and Crater Proculus

72-H-836 Far side King crater highlands
= AS16-120-19226

72-H-837 King Crater

72-H-839 Far side King Crater
=AS16-120-19228

72-H-1109 East of Mare Smythii

72-H-1113 Northwest of King Crater

72-H-1387 Lubinicky area
= LO-IV-125-H2

APPENDIX - 2
To Order NASA Moon Photos

Glossy 8 X 10 prints of all NASA Moon photographs identified in this book (and others if the full number is known) may be ordered directly from the NASA contractor: [Editor: rather order from the NSSDC Office., below']

Space Photographs
Post Office Box 486
Bladensburg, Maryland 20710

The NASA number should be given in full. The cost for a single 8 X 10 black and white photo is ~~$1.75; for color, $5.00.~~ All orders must be accompanied by a company check, certified check, or money order; personal checks are not acceptable. Postage and handling fees are ~~15% of order ($2.00 minimum) for the U.S. and Territories, and 30% of order ($5.00 minimum) for overseas.~~

[Now costs about $10 bucks!]

For other size photos or duplicates of the same subject write to Space Photographs for more extensive price quotations. The prices quoted above, according to the company, are expected to hold firm during the fiscal year beginning July 1, 1976; but they are subject to change.

For special research needs not furnished by Space

Photographs, or photos for use by the news media, contact or visit NASA at:

National Aeronautics and Space Administration
Room 6035
400 Maryland Avenue, S.W.
Washington, D. C. 20546 221

EDITOR'S ADDENDA: SOURCES OF LUNAR INFORMATION:

For hard copy prints and negatives of Lunar Orbiter Photographs, and other planetary missions:

NSSDC/Goddard Space Flight Center
Code 633
Greenbelt, MD. 20771 USA
WEB SITE:
http://science.nasa.gov/planetary-science/planetary-science-data/national-space-science-data-center-nssdc/

Photographic materials and other media may be inquired at:
http://www.nasa.gov/centers/hq/about/mailing_tips.html
NASA Headquarters
300 E Street SW
Washington DC 20024-3210

http://www.nasa.gov/centers/johnson/home/#.U1IxoqKwVWQ
Johnson Space Center
1601 NASA Parkway
Houstion, Texas 77058

281-244-2100

Public Communications and
Inquiries Management Office
NASA Headquarters
Suite 1M32
Washington, DC 20546-0001
(202) 358-0001 (Office)
(202) 358-3469 (Fax)
public-inquiries@hq.nasa.gov
+ Ask NASA

Please allow 10-15 business days for processing. For email inquiries, be sure to include a subject and do not include any attachments.

Source:

http://www.nasa.gov/about/contact/index

PHOTOGRAPHIC MATERIALS:

For web downloads of any photograph: Ranger, Lunar Orbiter and Apollo, see:

http://www.lpi.usra.edu/resources/lunar_orbiter/

LROC (Lunar Reconnaissance Orbiter Camera) IMAGE BROWSER:

http://wms.lroc.asu.edu/lroc_browse?page=1

Lunar Planetary Institute

http://www.lpi.usra.edu/lunar/lunar_images/

LUNAR RESOURCES:

http://www.lpi.usra.edu/resources/

LUNAR CAPTURES (IMAGES)
http://www.lunar-captures.com/software.html

LUNAR NETWORKS
(Excellent site for pictures and Selenological studies):
http://lunarnetworks.blogspot.com/2011/05/anomalous-mounds-on-floor-of-king.html

Bibliography

ASTRONOMY AND THE SOLAR SYSTEM

Asimov, Isaac, Asimov on Astronomy. Doubleday, 1974.

From Flat Earth to Quasar. Revised. Walker, 1971.

Cade, C. Maxwell, Other Worlds than Ours. New York, Tap- linger Publishing Co., 1967.

Calder, Nigel, Violent Universe. Viking, 1969.

Clarke, Arthur C., Report on Planet Three and Other Speculations. Harper and Row, 1972.

Voices from the Sky. Harper and Row, 1965.

Corliss, William R., Mysteries of the Universe. Crowell, 1967.

Dubridge, L. A., Introduction to Space. Columbia University Press, 1960.

Fesenkov, V., and A. Oparin, Life in the Universe. Twayne, 1961.

Filipowsky, R. F., Space Communications Techniques. Prentice* Hall, 1965.

Flammarion, C., Flammarion Book of Astronomy. New edition. Simon and Schuster, 1964.

Glasstone, Samuel, Sourcebook on the Space Sciences. Van Nostrand, 1965.

Hoyle, Fred, Astronomy. Doubleday, 1962.

Inglis, Stuart J., Planets, Stars and Galaxies: An Introduction to Astronomy. 3rd Ed. Wiley, 1972.

Kaula, William M., Introduction to Planetary Physics: The Terrestrial Planets. Wiley, 1968.

Ley, Willy, Conquest of Space. Viking, 1959.

Lyttleton, R. A., Mysteries of the Solar System. Oxford, 1968.

—, The Modern Universe. Harper, 1956.

MacVey, John W., Whispers from Space. Macmillan, 1973.

Page, T., and L. W. Page, Eds., Origin of the■ Solar System, Genesis of the Sun and Planets, and Life on Other Worlds, Sky And Telescope Library Of Astronomy, Vol. 3. Macmillan, 1966.

Riabchikov, E. I., Russians in Space. Doubleday, 1971. Richardson, Robert S., The Fascinating World Of Astronomy.

McGraw-Hill, 1960.

Sagan, Carl, Ed., Communication with Extraterrestrial Intelligence. M.I.T. Press, 1963.

Shlovskii, I. S., and Carl Sagan, Intelligent Life in the Universe.

Holden-Day, 1966.

Struve, Otto, pjid Velta Zebergs, Astronomy of the Twentieth Century. Macmillan, 1962.

Sullivan, Walter, We Are Not Alone. McGraw-Hill, 1964. Swart, William M., Riddle of the Universe. Longmans, 1968. Urey, H. C., Planets: Their Origin and Development. Yale University Press, 1952.

Von Braun, Werner, Space Frontier. New edition. Holt, 1971. Whipple, F. L., Earth, Moon and Planets. Harvard University Press, 3rd Ed., 1968.

THE MOON Books

("Alter, Dinsmore. Pictorial GuideJa the Moon. Crowell. 1967.

Cherrington,. Ernest H„ Exploring the Moon through Binoculars. McGraw-Hill, 1969.

Clarke, Arthur C., First on the Moon. Little, Brown and Co., 1970.

Cooper, Henry S. F., Apollo on the Moon. Dial, 1969.

Firsoff. V. A.. Strange World of the Moon, an Inquiry into Its Physical Features and the Possibility of Life. Basic, 1959.

Kennan, E. A., and E. H. Harvey, Jr., Mission to the Moon, Critical Examination of NASA and the Space Program. Morrow, 1969.

Kopol, Z., Ed., Physics and Astronomy of the Moon. Academic Press, 1960.

Kosofsky, L. J., and Farouk El-Baz, Moon as Viewed by Lunar Orbiter. NASA, 1970.

Moore, Patrick A., A Survey of the Moon. W. W. Norton, 1963.

National Aeronautics and Space Administration, Apollo Prelimi-

nary Science Reports (Apollo 12, Apollo 15, Apollo 16, Apollo 17). NASA, Washington, D.C.

NASA Facts: Manned Space Flight—The First Decade.

NASA, 1973.

Princeton University, Secondary School Science Project, Surface of the Moon, Records of the Past. McGraw-Hill, 1967. Simmons, Gene, On the Moon with Apollo 16. U.S Government Printing Office, 1972.

Whipple, F. L./The Nature of the Moon, 3rd edition.

Wilkins, H. P., and P. A. Moore, The Moon. Faber and Faber, 1960. .

Wilson, Don, Our Mysterious Spaceship Moon. Dell, 1975.

THE MOON Magazine and Journal Articles

American Astronomers Report: Highlights of Some Papers Presented at 113 th Meeting of American Astronautical Society, April 17-20, 1963," Sky And

Telescope,]uly, 1963.

Apollo 11 Science Conference Papers, Science Magazine, Jan. 30, 1970.

"Apollo 16 Photos Spur King Crater Study," Aviation Week, Sept. 25, 1972.

Cameron, W. S., "Observations of Changes on the Moon," Proceedings of the 5th Annual Meeting of Working Group on Extraterrestrial Resources, March 1-3, 1967 (NASA).

Comparative Analyses of Observations of Lunar Tran sient Phenomena," Icarus, 16, 339-387, 1972.

and J. J. Gilheanyr^tJperatlon Moon Blink and Report

of Observations of Lunar Transient Phenomena," Icarus, Vol. 7, No. 1, July, 1967.,

"Five Unexpected New Discoveries," Science Digest, Nov., 1970.

"Glazing the Moon," Time, Oct. 3, 1969.

Gold, T., "Skylab: Is It Worth the Risk and Expense?" (section titled "Does NASA Listen?".), Science and Public Affairs, Bulletin of the Atomic Scientists, Feb., 1974.

Goodavage, Joseph F., "What Strange—and Frightening— Discoveries Did Our Astronauts Make on the Moon?", Saga UFO Report, Winter, 1974.

"Isaac Asimov Explains Masccms," Science Digest, March, 197 L

Lowman, Paul D., Jr., "The Geologic Evolution of the Moon," Journal of Geology, March, 1972.

"Lunar Transient Phenomena," Aviation Week, March 3, 1969.

"The Moon Is More of a Mystery than Ever," The New York Times Magazine, April 16, 1972.

Moore, P. A., "Extension of the Chronological Catalogue of Reported Lunar Events: Oct. 1967-June 1971," Journal of the British Astronomical Association, 81, 5, 1971.

"More Light on Mascons," Science News, April 3, 1971. (Other articles on mascons—mass concentrations beneath the surface of the Moon which cause gravitational anomalies —are included in: Saturday Review, June 7, 1969, August 2, 1969; Science, Dec. 20, 1968, June 6, 1969, June 13, 1969, Aug. 15, 1969, Nov. 28, 1969.)

"Mysteries Remain," Newsweek, Feb. 1, 1971.

."Mysterious Moon," Scientific American, June, 1972.

National Aeronautics and Space Administration, "5th Lunar Science Conference," Sky And Telescope, August, 1974.

"The New Moon: Part I" (six articles by Urey, Sagan, et al.), Science and Public Affairs, Bulletin of the Atomic Scientists, Nov., 1973.

"New Theory on Craters," Science Digest, Oct., 1970.

"Riddle Of The Lunar Mountains," Space World, Aug., 1972.

"Some Mysteries Solved, Some Questions Raised," Time, Aug., 1969.

"Surprising Moon," Aviation Week, Oct. 25, 1971.

"Third Lunar Science Conference," Science News, Jan. 22, 1972.

Weaver, Kenneth F., "Have We Solved the Mysteries of the Moon?", National Geosravhic, Sept., 1973.

"Where Was thS'MooiTFormed? Science?Oct. 23, 1970.

PHENOMENA

Berlitz, Charles, The Bermuda Triangle. Doubleday, 1974.

The Bible.

Binder, Otto, What We Really Know about Flying Saucers.

Fawcett Gold Medal, 1967.

Bowen, Charles, The Humanoids (especially "The Problem of Non-Contact," by Aime Michel). London, Neville Spearman, 1969.

Charroux, Robert, One Hundred Thousand Years of Man's Unknown History. Berkley Medallion, 1970.

Condon, Edward TJ., Scientific Study of Unidentified Flying Objects. Bantam Paperback, 1969.

Edwards, Frank, "Scientists and Satellites," Fate, Feb., 1958.

Fort, Charles, Books of Charles Fort: New Lands, Lo!, The Book of the Damned, Wild Talents. Holt, Rinehart and Winston, 1941. Paperback editions issued by Ace Star Books.

Fuller, John G., The Interrupted Journey. Dial Press, 1966.

. Aliens in the Skies. Berkley, 1969.

Hall, Richard, Ed., The UFO Evidence. Washington, D.C. National Investigations Committee on Aerial Phenomena,

1964.

Holiday, F. W., Creatures from the Inner Sphere, W. W. Norton, 1973.

Hyneck, J. Allen, and Vallee, Jacques, The Edge of Reality. Regnery, 1975.

Jessup, M. K., The Case for the UFO. London, Arco Publications, 1956.

•, The Expanding Case for the UFO. London, Arco Publi

cations, 1957.

Jung, C. J., Flying Saucers: A Modern Myth of Things Seen in the Skies. Harcourt, Brace and World, 1959.

Keel, John A., Strange Creatures from Time and Space. Fawcett Gold Medal, 1970.

Knight, Damon, Charles Fort: Prophet of the Unexplained. Doubleday, 1970.

Le Poer Trench, Brinsley, The Flying Saucer Story. Ace, 1966.

Lorenzen, Coral E., The Shadow of the Unknown. Signet, 1970.

and Jim Lorenzen, Flying Saucer Occupants. Signet,

1967.

, UFO's Over the Americas. Signet, 1968.

— , UFO: The Whole Story. Signet, 1969.

, and Jim Lorenzen, Encounters with UFO Occupants.

Berkley, 1976.

Michell, John, The Flying Saucer Vision. Ace, 1967.

" Nicholson, John, "Little Green Men," Fantastic Universe, May, 1958.

" Norman, Eric, Gods, Demons, and UFO's. Lancer Books, 1970.

Ruppelt, E. J., The Report on Unidentified Flying Objects. Doubleday, 1958.

Sanderson, Ivan T., More "Things". Pyramid, 1969.

, Uninvited Visitors: A Biologist Looks at UFO's. London, Neville Spearman, 1969.

Saunders, David R., and R. Roger Harkins, UFO's? Yes! Where the Condon Committee Went Wrong. Signet, 1968. Steiger, Brad, Mysteries of Time and Space. Dell, 1974.

Vallee, Jacques, Anatomy of a Phenomenon. Henry Regnery,

1965.

, Passport to Magonia. Regnery, 1969.

, with Janine Vallee, Challenge to Science. Regnery, 1966.

Velikovsky, Immanuel, Worlds in Collision. Doubleday, 1950. Ward, Theodora, Men and Angels, a Personal Study of a Persisting Symbol in Western Culture. Viking, 1969.

SCIENCE, GENERAL

Asimov, Isaac, Fact and Fancy. Doubleday, 1962.

, Of Time, Space and Other Things. Doubleday, 1965.

, Is Anyone There? Doubleday, 1967.

, Science, Numbers and I. Doubleday, 1968.

Born, Max, The Restless Universe. Dover Publications, 1951.

de Ropp, Robert S., The New Prometheans. Delacorte Press, 1972.

Dubos, Rene, Reason, Awake. Science for Man. New York and London, Columbia University Press, 1970.

Einstein, Albert, Essays in Science. New York, Philosophic Library.

Eiseley, Loren, The Immense Journey. Vintage, 1957.

, The Unexpected Universe. Harcourt, Brace and World,

1969.

Moszkowski, Alex, Conversations with Einstein. Horizon, 1970.

Nininger, Harvey H., Find a Falling Star. Paul S. Eriksson, Inc., 1972.

Planck, Max, The New Science, Part I: "Where is Science Going?" Meridian Books, Inc., 1959.

Snow, C. P., The Two Cultures and the Scientific Revolution. Cambridge University Press, 1959.

Standen, Anthony, Science Is a Sacred Cow. E. P. Dutton, 1950.

Thompson, Paul D., Gases and Plasmas. Lippincott,

1966.

[EDITORS NOTE: The "Index" of subjects and page numbers is included but the page numbers have changes in re-publishing. They are close, but not accurate. See the original copy for original subject locations and page numbers.]

Index

Author:George H. Leonard

Keywords:UFO Moon Lunar surface artificial structures based on the moon NASA moon photographs

Collection: opensource

Description

Scientist George H. Leonard demonstrates the existence of artificial structures on the moon using NASA photographs of the lunar surface.

Selected metadata

Mediatype: texts

Licenseurl:
http://creativecommons.org/publicdomain/zero/1.0/

Identifier: SomebodyElseIsOnTheMoon

Identifier-access:
http://archive.org/details/SomebodyElseIsOnTheMoon

Identifier-ark: ark:/13960/t70v9nn1m

Ppi: 72

Ocr: ABBYY FineReader 8.0

ADVERTISEMENTS:

OTHER SOURCES LINKS:

Books, Tapes, Videos, DVD's documentaries: at Weirdvideos.com

https://www.createspace.com/Preview/1143454

BOOK ORDER INFORMATION AND QUESTIONS:

c/o Ross S. Marshall

P.O. Box 1191

Anacortes, Wa. 98221

ALIEN ARTIFACT SERIES:

Alien Artifacts, Volume-1

"Is Anyone Else on the Moon? The Search for Alien Artifacts According to George Leonard.

PREVIEW:

https://www.createspace.com/Preview/1145004

ORDER HERE!

http://www.amazon.com/dp/1495987760

Alien Artifacts, Volume-2

"Did We Really Discover Alien Bases on the Moon?" The Search for Alien Artifacts According to Fred Steckling.

"Moon Mars Monuments Madness." The Continued Search for Alien Garbage on the Moon and Mars According to Richard Hoagland.